MINITAB
Mini-Manual

A Beginner's Guide to Minitab

Second Edition

July 1995

ISBN 0-925636-31-2

We at Minitab Inc. wish to thank all who have contributed to the *MINITAB Mini-Manual*. We are especially grateful to Joan Carey, who wrote, compiled, and edited material in this book with such skill and good humor. We are also very grateful to the many reviewers who took the time to provide us with thoughtful and excellent suggestions.

Printed in the USA

1st Printing, 7/95

Table of Contents

Welcome

Welcome to Minitab Statistical Software

Minitab is a powerful statistical software package that provides a wide range of basic and advanced data analysis capabilities. Used at over 5,000 sites in 51 countries, including 2,000 schools, in 60 countries, Minitab has long been recognized as a leading developer of easy-to-use statistical software. Its straightforward command structure makes it accessible to users with a great variety of background and experience.

More college students are trained on Minitab than any other statistical software package. After these students graduate, they find their knowledge of Minitab valuable in their careers: for example, three-quarters of *Fortune*'s listing of the top 50 companies depend on Minitab for its unique combination of ease-of-use and powerful statistical and data management capabilities.

Purpose of this Manual

The *Minitab Mini-Manual* provides you with answers to most of the questions you will have as a new user of Minitab Statistical Software. Rather than fully documenting all features and functions, this manual explains the fundamentals of using Minitab—how to enter commands, how to manage data and files, how to manipulate and analyze data, how to produce graphs, how to use on-line Help—in a small, inexpensive book.

Minitab Statistical Software runs on PCs, Macintosh® computers, and most of the leading workstations, minicomputers, and mainframe computers. While Minitab differs across releases and computer platforms, most notably in ways that take advantage of platform-specific capabilities, the core of Minitab, the worksheet and commands, is the same. New releases do have new commands as well. But if you know how to use one release of Minitab on one platform, you can easily switch to another.

The examples in this manual were generated using Release 10*Xtra* of Minitab on a PC computer running Windows 3.1, with an emphasis on menu commands, but corresponding session commands are shown as well, which you can use with any version of the software. Chapter 2 is specifically written for session command users and users of earlier releases of Minitab.

This book is organized into six chapters and two appendices:

Chapter 1, Sample Session for Menu and Dialog Box Users

Chapter 1 is a sample Minitab session that gives a hands-on introduction to Minitab Statistical Software for Minitab releases with a menu and dialog box interface (including Macintosh and Windows from release 8 on and Release 10 or later for all other platforms). You assume the role of data analyst as you follow the steps one might take in examining data on exercise patterns and the physical condition of college students.

Chapter 2, Sample Session for Command Users

Chapter 2 is a sample Minitab session that gives a hands-on introduction to Minitab Statistical Software for Minitab releases with a command-line interface (including all releases earlier than release 8 and release 9 for mini/mainframes) or for users of any release who want to learn Minitab session commands. You assume the role of data analyst as you follow the steps one might take in examining data on exercise patterns and the physical condition of college students. The commands covered in this chapter are identical to those covered in Chapter 1.

Chapter 3, Overview of Minitab

Chapter 3 introduces you to Minitab's worksheet and command structure. It explains how to start and stop Minitab, how to use the Minitab interface, including menus, dialog boxes, and session commands, and how to get on-line Help. It also discusses alpha and numeric data and special Minitab symbols and prompts.

Chapter 4, Managing Data

Chapter 4 has the dual purpose of showing you how to get data into Minitab, and how to manage it once it's there. The first part covers entering data, using both the Data window and session commands, naming columns, navigating and correcting the worksheet, and entering patterned data. The file management part of the chapter shows you how to save and retrieve Minitab worksheets, how to get data from other applications in and out of Minitab, how to create an outfile to save output and commands, and finally, how to print hard copies of your work. Commands are shown for both menu and dialog box users and session command users.

Chapter 5, Manipulating and Analyzing Data

Chapter 5 samples some of Minitab's most frequently used statistical analysis commands, including plenty of examples. It begins with a few data manipulation techniques, including copying, sorting, and coding columns. It also covers arithmetic transformations, basic descriptive statistics, t-confidence intervals, t-tests, correlation, regression, analysis of variance, cross-tabulation (categorized summaries of data), and χ^2 analysis. Commands are shown for both menu and dialog box users and session command users.

Chapter 6, Graphics

Chapter 6 illustrates the most common Minitab graphics commands, including scatter plots, histograms, boxplots, and statistical process control charts. It also covers the basics of saving and printing graphs.

Appendix A

Appendix A is a quick reference that offers an overview of Minitab and its interface, the Data window and data and file management, all Minitab commands and subcommands, quality control and graphics tools, and a keyboard shortcut reference.

Appendix B

Appendix B describes and lists the data in the Minitab worksheet PULSE.MTW, used in the sample sessions in Chapters 1 and 2.

How to Use this Manual

This manual begins by giving you immediate hands-on experience using Minitab in Chapters 1 and 2, sample sessions using menu and dialog box commands and then session commands, respectively. You begin by opening, exploring, modifying, and saving a worksheet, and then trying some of Minitab's statistical commands. The session should take you less than an hour. You will need the sample file PULSE.MTW that is included with all versions and releases of Minitab (and is listed in Appendix B). If you don't know where to find it, ask your System Administrator.

To learn Minitab most efficiently after you've practiced with the sample session, turn to Chapter 3, *Overview of Minitab*. It explains Minitab fundamentals, as well as how to use this manual hand-in-hand with Minitab's on-line Help.

You can proceed through the rest of the manual however it best suits your needs. Chapter 4 explains how to get data in and out of Minitab and the file types, and Chapters 5 and 6 give you a sample of Minitab's analysis and graphics capabilities. When you are ready to explore commands not covered in this manual, consult Appendix A, an overview of Minitab and a complete list of all Minitab commands, organized by topic. To find out how to use these commands, you can use on-line Help. The *MINITAB Reference Manual* (see the *Documentation* section that follows) gives complete coverage of all Minitab commands, but Help will answer many of your questions about how Minitab functions.

Assumptions

This manual assumes that you know the basics of getting around the computer platform you are using, be it a mainframe, a PC, or a Macintosh. If you do not feel comfortable with these skills, refer to user documentation on your computer.

Other Documentation

To help you learn to use Minitab, this manual includes Appendix A, *Quick Reference*, in the back of the book. The software itself provides on-line Help (explained in Chapter 3, *Overview of Minitab*) that goes beyond the introductory scope of this manual.

In addition to on-line Help and this manual, Minitab also offers four especially helpful documents that you can order by phone or by using the information in the back of this book:

MINITAB Reference Manual, Minitab Inc.

This is a comprehensive guide, available for different releases, on how to use Minitab. It contains detailed explanations of all Minitab commands and subcommands.

MINITAB Handbook, Third Edition, 1994, Duxbury Press, Belmont, CA

This is a supplementary textbook that shows, by example, how to use Minitab to perform a variety of statistical analyses. It contains numerous case studies and exercises that show, step-by-step, how to use Minitab to analyze data.

MINITAB Quick Reference, Minitab Inc.

This is a summary, available for different releases, of all Minitab commands in a convenient, small booklet, similar to Appendix A in this manual.

Companion Textbook List, Minitab Inc.

More than 300 textbooks and textbook supplements which include Minitab have been published. For a complete bibliography organized by discipline and level (introductory, intermediate, and advanced), contact your distributor or Minitab Inc.

Technical Support

Register as a Minitab User

One phone call is all it takes. Contact your distributor or call Minitab Inc. between 8:30 a.m. and 5:30 p.m. Eastern time, Monday through Friday. If you are calling from within the U.S. or Canada, call 800-448-3555. Otherwise, call 814-238-3280, or contact Minitab Inc. at the address listed in the back of this manual.

Registered Minitab users are eligible to receive technical support, new product announcements, update reports, the *KeepingTAB Newsletter*, and the *MINITAB Users' Group Newsletter*, which contains useful articles, tips, and macros.

Distributors

Several distributors provide full sales and support services to Minitab customers in Europe, in the Asia-Pacific region, and Latin America. See *Minitab Distributors* in the back of this manual for a list of distributors and contact information.

Customer Support

A highly skilled staff of technical specialists is available to answer your questions quickly and thoroughly, by telephone, mail, and fax. For technical help or additional product information, registered users can contact their distributor or Minitab Inc., 3081 Enterprise Drive, State College, PA 16801-3008, phone 814-231-2682 (2MTB), fax 814-238-4383.

A Quick Guide to Minitab Features

This section gives you a quick overview of Minitab features. Use this guide to skim or review Minitab capabilities, or when you are not sure whether Minitab can do something. You may find features to help you solve problems you never thought Minitab could help you with.

General

- **Complete menu interface**
- **Interactive command-line option**
- **Context-sensitive on-line Help for all dialog boxes**
- **On-line Help for all session commands, plus many of the conceptual overviews from the *MINITAB Reference Manual***
- **On-line glossary of terms**
- **On-line and *MINITAB Reference Manual* examples** that show both dialog boxes and command language along with a full on-line showcase of Minitab graphs
- **QuickStart tutorials that cover a variety of Minitab capabilities**
- **Powerful yet easy-to-use macro programming language** with IF, ELSEIF, and ELSE statements, WHILE and DO loops, GOTO statements, PAUSE and RESUME, ability to assemble your own commands with subcommands
- **Improved speed via 32-bit architecture (Minitab for Windows Release 10*Xtra* Only)**
- **Interactive and batch modes of operation**
- **Free technical support for the life of the product**

Data and File Management

- **Import/Export capabilities include:**
  - direct interface with Lotus 1-2-3, Excel, Quattro Pro, dBASE, FoxPro, ASCII
  - Preview screen allows you to select the data to import from a file and choose where to place it in the Minitab worksheet (for Microsoft Windows Only)
  - merge worksheet—merge Minitab, Lotus 1-2-3, Excel, Quattro Pro, dBASE, FoxPro, and/or ASCII files into the current worksheet
  - portable worksheet format for exchanging data between Minitab releases and platforms
- **Dynamic Data Exchange (DDE) (for Microsoft Windows Only)**
  - act as server and/or client to receive and/or send data automatically
  - can update data only, update data and run an analysis automatically, or not update data
  - cold link capability for one-time command execution or data update
  - send data to other packages
  - send data to other packages and run additional analyses automatically
  - automatic column recalculation from within Minitab

- **Data Editor**
  - enter, view, or edit data using cut, copy, paste, delete
  - edit or move entire variables, blocks of data, or single cells
  - enter values in a specified range of the worksheet

- **Name stored constants and matrices**

- **Data manipulation**—merge, stack, subset, sort, rank, unconditional and conditional copy, and delete

- **Arithmetic and logical operators**—standardize, absolute value, square root, natural log, log base 10, exponential, power, trigonometric functions, inverse trigonometric functions, partial sums and partial products, AND, OR, NOT

- **Matrix operations**—transpose, inverse, eigenvalues, eigenvectors

Session Window Editing

- **Change existing text and add comments** anywhere in the Session window, or if desired, make the Session window read-only

- **Suppress display and/or entry of command language** if desired

- **Command Line Editor** lets you edit an entire sequence of commands, then submit them all at once (you can also paste to the command prompt to do this)

- **Save session output easily**
  - save all output from a session automatically, overwrite or append to output from previous sessions
  - start/stop output files (outfiles) as needed

- **Use different fonts** for output, titles of output, and added comments

- **Select columns of output and rectangular areas** for cutting, copying, and pasting

- **Change prompt color** for increased visibility if desired

Basic Statistics

- **Descriptive statistics**
  - count, mean, median, standard deviation, standard error of mean, quartiles, minimum, maximum, range
  - skewness, kurtosis
  - graphical descriptive statistics: a display in a Graph window which includes a histogram with overlaid normal curve, a boxplot, confidence intervals for the mean, median, and standard deviation, and a table of statistics

- **Inferential statistics**
  - confidence intervals, one- and two-sample t-tests, paired t-tests
  - homogeneity of variance test

- **Goodness-of-Fit Tests**
  - tests for normality: Anderson-Darling, Ryan-Joiner (similar to Shapiro-Wilk), and Kolmogorov-Smirnov
  - Chi-square goodness-of-fit test

- **Cross tabulations**
- **Correlation and covariance matrices, partial correlations**

Regression Analysis

- **Simple and multiple regression models**
- **Model selection using forward, backward, or stepwise regression**
- **Best subsets regression**
- **Weighted least squares**
- **X-Y scatter plot with fitted regression line, confidence bands, and prediction bands**
- **Comprehensive summary of fitted model**—coefficients, standard errors, t-statistics, p-values, ANOVA table, identification of unusual observations
- **Prediction/confidence intervals for new observations using user-specified confidence levels**
- **Full set of regression diagnostics**—residuals, fits, standardized residuals, deleted t residuals, Cook's distance, leverages, DFITS, X'X matrix, R matrix, Durbin-Watson statistic, lack-of-fit test
- **Residual diagnostic plot**—includes histogram and normal plot of residuals, plot of residuals vs. fits, individuals control chart of residuals for detecting non-random patterns and outliers

Analysis of Variance (ANOVA)

- **One-way and two-way ANOVA**—for balanced designs
- **Tukey, Fisher, Dunnett, and MCB** multiple comparison methods for one-way ANOVA
- **Analysis of Means (ANOM)**—use with normal, binomial, and Poisson response variables
- **Multiple factor ANOVA**—for balanced designs with fixed and random effects, crossed and nested factors
  - expected mean squares for random effects models
  - Hotelling's T^2 test
- **General linear models (GLM)**—for balanced or unbalanced designs, crossed and nested factors
- **Multivariate analysis of variance (MANOVA)**
- **Analysis of covariance (ANCOVA)**
- **Comprehensive summary of fitted models**—including ANOVA table, sequential sums of squares, identification of unusual observations
- **Full set of ANOVA diagnostics**—including residuals, fits, standardized residuals, deleted t residuals, Cook's distance, leverages, DFITS, X matrix
- **Residual diagnostics plot**—includes histogram and normal plot of residuals, plot of residuals vs. fits, individuals control chart of residuals for detecting non-random patterns and outliers
- **Main effects plot**—displays influences of up to 50 factors on a response variable
- **Interaction effects plot**—displays two-way interaction effects for up to 9 factors

Multivariate Analysis

- **Principle components analysis**—uses either correlation or covariance matrix as input, displays eigenvalues and proportion of total variance for each component

- **Linear and quadratic discriminant analysis**
  - user can specify prior probabilities
  - uses cross-validation method to compensate for optimistic apparent error rate
  - predicts group membership for new observations

- **Cluster analysis**
  - hierarchical analysis of observations and variables
  - K-means analysis
  - dendrogram

- **Factor analysis**
  - maximum likelihood and principle components methods of extraction
  - uses data, correlation or covariance matrix, or loadings as input
  - varimax, equamax, orthomax, and quartimax rotations

Time Series Analysis

- **Time series plot** (with options as shown under *General Graphics*)

- **Trend analysis**
  - linear, quadratic, exponential growth, S-curve models
  - fit model, generate forecasts, detrend data
  - combine information from prior trend analyses for comparison with current data

- **Decomposition analysis**
  - multiplicative or additive models
  - use trend and seasonal components, detrended and seasonally adjusted data, fits, residuals, forecasts
  - unique graphical displays enhance understanding of various components

- **Single exponential smoothing**
  - smoothed values, fits, residuals, forecasts, forecast prediction intervals
  - optimal parameter selection, or user-specified parameters

- **Double exponential smoothing**
  - fit Holt or Brown models
  - smoothed values, level and trend components, fits, residuals, forecasts, forecast prediction intervals
  - optimal selection of parameters, or user-specified parameters

- **Winters' method**
  - multiplicative or additive models
  - smoothed values, level, trend, and seasonal components, fits, residuals, forecasts, forecast prediction intervals

- **Moving average**—moving average, fits, residuals, forecasts, forecast prediction intervals

- **ACF, PACF, CCF**
  - new graphical ACF adds Ljung-Box Q statistic, confidence bands
  - new graphical PACF adds confidence bands
- **Univariate Box-Jenkins ARIMA analysis**
  - seasonal and nonseasonal models
  - fits, residuals, forecasts, forecast prediction intervals
- **Lag, lead, and difference transformation**

Nonparametrics

- **Sign test and confidence interval (one sample)**
- **Wilcoxon test and confidence interval (one sample)**
- **Mann-Whitney test and confidence interval (two sample)**
- **Kruskal-Wallis test (k sample)**
- **Friedman test for two-way layout**
- **Runs test**
- **Spearman rank correlation**
- **Walsh averages, differences, and slopes**
- **Mood's median test (k samples)**

Simulation and Distributions

- **Random number generator**—generates any number of values with specifiable parameters for normal, lognormal, Weibull, exponential, beta, gamma, chi-squared, t, F, uniform, Cauchy, Laplace, logistic, Bernoulli, binomial, Poisson, and integer distributions
- **Probability Density Function (PDF), Cumulative Distribution Function (CDF), Inverse Cumulative Distribution Function (INVCDF)**
- **Random sampling with or without replacement**

Statistical Process Control

- **Run chart**—performs two tests for randomness to detect mixture patterns, clusters, oscillation, and trend, providing you with information regarding the influence of special causes on your process
- **Pareto charts**—use raw data or counts for each category
  - allows a group (BY) variable to generate charts for different groups, either all on the same page, or on different pages
  - can combine smallest bars below a specified percentage into a single bar
- **Cause-and-effect/Fishbone diagram**

- **Variables control charts**—Xbar, R, S, I, MR, MA, EWMA, CUSUM, ZONE
  - Zone chart—incorporates several Shewhart runs rules into one simple scoring system, with a single rule to determine when a process is out of control
  - obtain control limits using pooled standard deviation, Rbar (MRbar) or historical parameters
  - eight tests for special causes (Xbar, I)
  - data display, annotation, frame, and regions graphics options for all control chart commands
- **Attributes control charts**—p, np, c, u
  - obtain control limits from data or historical parameters
  - four tests for special causes
  - data display, annotation, frame, and regions graphics options for all control chart commands
- **Combination control charts**—Xbar-R, Xbar-S, I-MR, Z-MR
  - Short run chart (Z-MR)—analyze the data coming off a machine, even if it comprises multiple products; generate an individual and a moving range (MR) chart of standardized (Z) values from a short run process
- **Process capability analysis**
  - capability histogram with normal curve overlay
  - table of statistics includes: Cp, CPU, CPL, Cpk, Cpm, % out of spec, PPM out of spec
- **Process Capability Sixpack graph**—unique all-in-one visual display combines six charts to verify process stability, check normality of data, and graphically describe process capability

Design of Experiments (DOE)

- **Factorial designs**—two-level full and fractional factorials for up to 15 factors
  - automatic design generation, or complete user control over confounding relations
  - automatic blocking arrangements, or complete user control over block generators
  - support for folded designs, nonorthogonal designs, additional center points
  - replicates and randomization
- **Plackett-Burman designs**—for up to 47 factors
- **Factorial model fit**
  - coefficients and effects for factors and interactions, ANOVA table, sequential sums of squares, identification of unusual observations
  - include/exclude any factors/interactions from model
  - tests for curvature and lack of fit
  - include covariates in model
  - residuals, fits, standardized residuals, deleted t residuals, Cook's distance, leverages, DFITS, X matrix
- **Response surface designs**
  - central composite designs for up to 6 factors
  - Box-Behnken designs for up to 7 factors
- **Response surface regression**
  - coefficients, ANOVA table, sequential sums of squares, identification of unusual observations
  - test for lack of fit
  - include covariates in model
  - residuals, fits, standardized residuals, deleted t residuals, Cook's distance, leverages, DFITS, X matrix

- **Response surface plots** for fitted response surface models
  - contour plot
  - 3D surface plot
  - 3D wireframe plot

- **Mixture designs**
  - simplex centroid designs for up to 7 factors
  - simplex lattice designs for up to 15 factors
  - generate designs in natural units, proportions, or pseudo-components
  - use lower bound constraints

- **Fit Scheffé mixture model**
  - linear, quadratic, special cubic, full cubic models
  - coefficients, ANOVA table, sequential sums of squares, identification of unusual observations
  - residuals, fits, standardized residuals, deleted *t* residuals, Cook's distance, leverages, DFITS, X matrix

- **Residual diagnostics plot**—including histogram and normal plot of residuals, plot of residuals vs. fits, individuals control chart of residuals for detecting non-random patterns and outliers

- **Main effects plot**—displays influences of up to 50 factors on a response variable

- **Interactions plot**—displays two-way interaction effects for up to 9 factors

General Graphics

- **Plots**—including scatter, line, LOWESS, area, and projection plots
  - slightly move (or jitter) points that overlap to see overlapping points
  - easily generate high-low-close plots
  - data display, annotation, frame, and regions graphics options

- **Time series plots**—including line, LOWESS, symbol, area, and projection plots
  - generate graphs with multiple time unit axes (for example, having separate scales for Second/Minute/Hour, or Month/Quarter/Year)
  - vary start times
  - data display, annotation, frame, and regions graphics options

- **Charts**—including line, bar, area, symbol, and projection charts
  - graph functions of y-axis variable, including: sum, n, nmissing, count, standard deviation, median, minimum, maximum, or sums of squares
  - group data into clusters or stacks, use percentage scales, make cumulative charts, show groups in increasing or decreasing order
  - data display, annotation, frame, and regions graphics options

- **Histograms**—including bar, line, LOWESS, area, symbol, and projection histograms
  - adjust midpoints/cutpoints, cumulative histograms, density histograms, or use percent scales
  - data display, annotation, frame, and regions graphics options
  - easy to construct histograms with distribution curves (histogram with normal curve, etc.)

- **Boxplots**—use adjustable confidence intervals, interquartile ranges, or the entire range of values for boxes
  - make proportional width boxes
  - data display, annotation, frame, and regions graphics options

- **Matrixplots and Draftsman plots**—including scatter, line, LOWESS, area, and projection plots
  - show entire matrix or just upper-right or lower-left sections
  - slightly move (or jitter) points that overlap to see overlapping points
  - data display, annotation, frame, and regions graphics options

- **Contour plots**—including line and area contour plots
  - optionally specify either the number of levels, or the values for contour levels
  - optionally customize mesh positions to improve either resolution or performance
  - data display, annotation, frame, and regions graphics options
  - use Make Mesh Data function to quickly assemble a grid for entering contour data

- **Pie charts**—use raw data or counts for each category
  - start slices at any angle, slices in increasing order, decreasing order, or order of occurrence
  - combine smallest slices below a specified percentage into a single slice
  - display frequency, percentage, frequency and percentage, or no labels
  - specify slice and label colors, label size, monochrome charts, and draw lines to labels

- **Interval charts for means**—display standard error bars or confidence intervals for categories
  - display standard error bars, or filled bars that extend from the x-axis
  - symbol, line, and bar options

- **Marginal plots**—scatter plots with histograms, boxplots, or dotplots, on one or both axes
  - symbol, frame, and label options

- **Normal probability plot** with Anderson-Darling and Ryan-Joiner goodness-of-fit tests

- **Weibull probability plot**

- **Layouts**—combine several graphs on a page, make text charts

- **Character graphs**—including histograms, stem-and-leaf plots, boxplots, dotplots, scatter plots, multiple scatter plots, pseudo three-dimensional plots, time series plots, multiple time series plots, contour plots, and grids for character contour plots

- **Many more discipline-specific graphs**—Pareto charts, main effects plots, interaction plots, residuals plots, fitted line plots all under their respective statistical areas

- **Manage graphs**—open, save, close, print, copy, rename, tile, restore, minimize, and maximize graphs from one convenient dialog box (for Microsoft Windows Only)

Graphics Options

- **Data display options**—give you the flexibility to display points on a graph in one or more different ways, allow you to display groups of points or individual points in different ways
  - **Symbols**—display points as symbols, change symbols for individual points or groups of points, use letters as symbols, use symbol labels, change symbol color and size

- **Connection lines**—connect all points or groups of points with lines; change line type, color, or width; connect plots with steplike lines or in different orders
- **LOWESS lines**—connect smoothed points or groups of points with a line, adjust the f value, adjust influence of outliers, store fitted and residual values for the smoothed line, change line type, color, or width
- **Projection lines**—extend lines from points to axes or defined bases, change direction of projection lines, change line color, line type, or line width
- **Areas**—fill the area under all points or under groups of points, make step-like areas, change color or fill type of areas, change edge line color, edge line type, edge line width
- **Bars**—display points on charts and histograms as bars, change bar width, bar fill color, fill type, edge color, edge type, and edge width
- **Boxes**—display interquartile ranges, customizable confidence intervals, or the entire range of values; make box width proportional to number of observations; change box width, change box color or fill type, change edge color, edge type, edge width

- **Graph annotation options**—place, rotate, and offset any number of titles, footnotes, text strings, or marker symbols using different fonts, colors, and sizes; also see *Graph Editing* features

- **Frame customization options**
  - change color, size, and rotation of text labels; color, width, and placement of axis, tick, grid, and reference lines
  - change minimum and maximum values on x- or y-scales
  - change number and orientation of ticks

- **Region and multiple graph options**
  - generate many graphs from one dialog box/command, or overlay graphs to make a single graph
  - keep the scale the same across multiple graphs
  - change size and aspect ratio of graphs
  - fill the interiors of different graph regions, and customize region edge lines

Three-Dimensional Graphs

- **Three-dimensional scatter plots**—use symbols, projection lines, and change viewing and rendering options

- **Three-dimensional surface plots**—use symbols, projection lines, and change viewing, lighting, and rendering options
  - optionally customize mesh positions to improve either resolution or performance
  - use Make Mesh Data function to quickly assemble a grid for entering surface data

- **Three-dimensional wireframe plots**—use symbols, projection lines, and change viewing, lighting, and rendering options
  - optionally customize mesh positions to improve either resolution or performance
  - use Make Mesh Data function to quickly assemble a grid for entering wireframe data

Three-Dimensional Graph Options

- **Viewing options**—move around graphs to view them from all sides and orientations, zoom in and out from graphs, adjust aspect ratios, use perspective or orthographic projections, and view graphs with full, partial, or no boundary boxes

- **Lighting options**—use up to 100 lights to highlight and illuminate different areas on the graph or to improve the accuracy or performance of surface rendering, change brightness of lights

- **Rendering options**
  - use z-sort, painters, or software z-buffer hidden surface removal methods, or choose no hidden surface removal to improve accuracy or performance
  - use flat, Gourand, or Phong light shading methods, or use no light shading method to improve accuracy or performance

- **Make mesh data**—generate a mesh for data collection for surface, wireframe, or contour plots, or generate data that fit a specified function; choose from many Minitab-supplied functions, or design your own functions

Graph Editing

- **Draw new objects**—symbols, lines, polylines, circles, ellipses, squares, rectangles, or polygons anywhere on a graph and edit their colors, fills, sizes, line types, or line widths

- **Text**—put text anywhere on the graph in different fonts, colors, and sizes

- **Modify existing graph objects**—move, resize, delete, or change attributes of any object generated with the graph

- **Resize text and objects** and reformat text into different size areas

- **Multiple objects**—select and move multiple objects

- **Align** objects and text with each other or with the entire graph page

- **Flip and rotate** objects and text

- **Copy and paste** objects between Graph windows, paste text from most other windows into a Graph window

- **Use custom colors** for any graph object

- **Duplicate** either a single object or all objects in a selection

- **Bring to front/send to back** objects in the same layer of the graph

- **Lock/unlock data objects**—keep graph data objects locked so you don't change them accidentally, or unlock them to move them if you wish

Graph Brushing

- **Identify characteristics of graph points**, or groups of points, by highlighting the points

- **Use up to ten indicator variables** to show characteristics of highlighted graph points

- **Brush across different Graph windows**—when you brush points in one graph, the points in other graphs are highlighted automatically
- **Change highlight color** for brushed points
- **Use Graph Editing to modify brushed points**

1

Sample Session for Menu and Dialog Box Users

- **Start Minitab**
- **Save, retrieve, and view data**
- **Correct the worksheet by changing and adding data**
- **Get on-line Help**
- **Look at data graphically with dotplots, box-and-whisker plots, and scatter plots**
- **Compute basic descriptive statistics**
- **Perform statistical analysis, including analysis of variance and t-tests**
- **Plot a fitted regression line**

How to Use the Sample Session

Chapters 1 and 2 are hands-on introductions to Minitab statistical software. Chapter 1 uses the menus and dialog boxes available with recent releases of Minitab while Chapter 2 uses the session commands available in all releases.

Release 6 and 7	Session commands only
Release 8 for Macintosh and DOS	Menu and dialog box availability
Release 9 for mini/mainframes	Session commands only
Release 9 for Windows	Menu and dialog box availability
Release 10 for Macintosh and Windows	Menu and dialog box availability

If your release supports only session commands, skip this chapter and use the Chapter 2 sample session. Otherwise, you can work through the sample session in Chapter 1, and then either skip Chapter 2 or proceed through it if you would like experience working with session commands. Both Chapters 1 and 2 use the same data and analysis methods.

By working through the sample session, you assume the role of the data analyst not only to experience a normal Minitab session, but also to learn your way around Minitab. The sample session starts with the basics of opening, exploring, modifying, and saving a worksheet. Later in the session you will try some of Minitab's statistical commands. The commands used in this session are covered in detail in later chapters of this manual.

Getting Started Using Minitab

You will need the Minitab worksheet PULSE.MTW that comes with the sample data in every release of Minitab. If, even after following the directions in this session, you can't find this file, see your System Administrator or call Minitab for help. Appendix B contains a description and listing of the data. To proceed through the session, follow the instructions in **boldface**. If you find slight discrepancies between what you see on your screen and the output shown throughout the sample session, don't worry. We are probably just using different versions of Minitab. Windows and dialogs for Release 8 in particular look a bit different. This session requires a mouse.

The Experiment

Measuring pulse rates before and after vigorous activity is one way to assess a person's physical condition. Many things affect what kind of shape we are in, including diet, daily exercise, and habits like smoking or drinking. Students in an introductory statistics course decided to explore their own physical condition in relation to a few of these variables.

Each student in the class recorded his or her height, weight, gender, smoking preference, usual activity level, and resting pulse. Then they participated in a simple experiment: the students all flipped coins, and those whose coins came up heads ran in place for one minute. Then the entire class recorded their pulses once more.

One of the students volunteered to enter the data on the record sheets into Minitab, one variable in each column (designated by C1, C2, etc., with column names in single quotes, like C6 'HEIGHT'). The resulting Minitab worksheet contained the following information:

Variable	Description
C1 'PULSE1'	Resting pulse rate
C2 'PULSE2'	Second pulse rate
C3 'RAN'	1 = ran in place 2 = did not run in place
C4 'SMOKES'	1 = smokes regularly 2 = does not smoke regularly
C5 'SEX'	1 = male 2 = female
C6 'HEIGHT'	Height in inches
C7 'WEIGHT'	Weight in pounds
C8 'ACTIVITY'	Usual level of physical activity: 1 = slight 2 = moderate 3 = a lot

The volunteer who entered the data saved the worksheet as PULSE.MTW. Now it's up to you to start looking for trends in the data. See Appendix B for a listing of the data set.

Starting Minitab

Begin by starting Minitab. If you aren't sure how to use a mouse or how to navigate menus and dialog boxes, see page 3-4.

Locate and open the Minitab program group or folder.

Double-click the blue Minitab icon that looks something like the following (Release 8 MS-DOS users should type minitab at the command prompt):

Minitab 10.5
Xtra

Retrieving Data from a Worksheet File

Now retrieve the Minitab saved worksheet named PULSE.MTW.

Choose File ➤ Open Worksheet. To do this, click File and drag down until your pointer is on Open Worksheet, then release the mouse button.

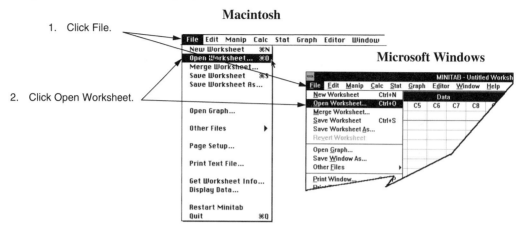

The Open Worksheet dialog box opens.

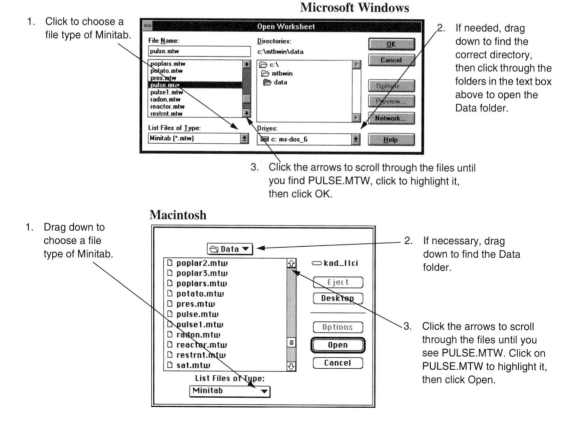

When you click OK, the file opens and appears in the Data window.

Viewing Data

If it is not already visible, open the Data window to view your worksheet.

Choose Window ➤ Data (for DOS 8, type Alt + D). The Data window appears and becomes active.

You can see some of the columns and the data. To get an idea of what the worksheet contains, you can check the Info window, which lists the variables in the current worksheet and their names, the number of rows in each column, and information on constants and matrices.

Choose Window ➤ Info (DOS 8, press Alt + D and type INFO). This gives a summary of the PULSE.MTW worksheet.

The columns in the worksheet correspond to the data gathered by the class.

Starting Your Analysis

There are a number of different approaches you could take to this data set. You decide to start by examining C1 PULSE1, the variable containing the first pulse reading (that is, resting pulse). Is there any variation, perhaps by activity level? Previous medical research suggests that the more active people are, the lower their resting pulses are. Is this true for this class?

Looking at a Dotplot

Most statisticians feel that it is good statistical practice to begin analysis by looking at the data graphically. You decide to look at the distribution of the students' resting pulses by activity level by generating a dotplot, with the Dotplot command.

Choose Graph ➤ Character Graphs ➤ Dotplot (Release 8, **Graph ➤ Dotplot**). To do this, click Graph, then click Character Graphs, then click Dotplot. The Dotplot dialog box opens.

Double-click PULSE1 in the selection list to place it in the Variables box. PULSE1, which contains resting pulses, is the variable Minitab will plot.

Click the By variable check box, click the corresponding text box, and then double-click ACTIVITY. Minitab will show the resting pulses by activity level.

The Dotplot dialog box should look like this:

Click OK. Minitab produces the following dotplot in the Session window. Choose **Window ➤ Session** (or DOS 8, press [Alt]+[M]) if you can't see the Session window.

The dotplots don't offer much conclusive evidence, although you can see that most of the students classified their activity level as "moderate," or activity level 2. Recall that level 1 is "slight" and 3 is "a lot" of physical activity. All three groups have resting pulse readings that vary quite a bit.

Correcting the Worksheet

But what is activity level 0 on the first dotplot? Checking back to the data set description, you notice that there shouldn't be a level 0. Moreover, it corresponds with a resting pulse of 48, a rather low reading. The person entering the data could have made a few mistakes—easy enough to do, and something that statisticians must always watch for. The entry of 0 could have a significant effect on your subsequent analysis.

Making Global Changes Using Code Data Values

You decide to delete the 0 activity level and replace it with the missing value symbol, an asterisk (*), since you're not sure what it should be. One way to change the 0 to * is by using the **Manip ➤ Code Data Values** command. Tell Minitab to replace every 0 it finds in the column ACTIVITY with the symbol *, and put it back in the same column.

Choose Manip ➤ Code Data Values (Release 8, **Calc ➤ Code Data Values**). The Code Data Values dialog box opens.

Double-click ACTIVITY to place it in the Code data from columns text box, and then press Tab.

Double-click ACTIVITY to place it in the Into columns text box. This tells Minitab to place the coded data back into the same column.

Click the first Original values text box, and then type 0. This tells Minitab to search for all values of "0" in the ACTIVITY column.

Press Tab, **and then type** *. This tells Minitab to replace the values it finds with the * symbol.

The Code Data Values dialog box should look like this:

Click OK. To verify that Minitab has changed the 0 to an *, check the Info window again.

Choose **Window ➤ Info** (DOS 8, type INFO in the Session window). The Info window now shows one missing value in C8. It looks like you've taken care of the problem.

Changing Cell Values

You still need to decide how to handle the surprisingly low resting pulse entry of 48 that corresponded to the 0 activity level. Leafing back through the survey sheets the students turned in, you are able to find the sheet corresponding with this person (luckily the person entering the data kept the pile of record sheets in order). There you find that student failed to enter an activity level (which may be why it was entered as 0), and that the resting pulse should have been 58, not 48. To fix this mistake, found in row 54 of the data set, use the Data window. If the Data window is not visible, choose **Window ➤ Data** to display it.

Scroll down to row 54. To do this, click the down scroll arrow.

Click cell C1, row 54, which contains the value 48. The value is highlighted. Anything you type will replace the cell contents.

data entry arrow

Active cell is highlighted.

Click the down scroll arrow to move through the worksheet.

Type 58, and then press Enter. The value you typed replaces the old value.

You could repeat the DOTPLOT command if you want to take another look at the data set with the corrections made.

Inserting Data

Just as you think you have the worksheet all tidied up, your professor informs you that two students who missed class the day of the experiment want their data included. The two students report the following data:

PULSE1	PULSE2	RAN	SMOKES	SEX	HEIGHT	WEIGHT	ACTIVITY
73	84	1	2	1	65	138	2
72	70	2	2	1	72	185	3

The Info window showed that there are presently 92 rows in the worksheet, so add the two new cases in rows 93 and 94.

Press Ctrl + End **(** Home **+** ↓ **for Macintosh) to move to the last cell in the worksheet.** To do this, press and hold down Ctrl and then press End.

Click the data entry arrow so it points to the right. The previous illustration shows the location of the data entry arrow. Now you can enter the data by row rather than by column.

Press Ctrl + Enter **(** ⌘ **+** Enter **for Macintosh,** F6 **for DOS) to move to the beginning of the next row.**

Type 73, press Enter **, type 84, press** Enter **, type 1, press** Enter **, and continue until you have entered all the values in the first row.**

Press Ctrl + Enter **(** ⌘ **+** Enter **for the Macintosh,** F6 **for DOS) to move to the beginning of the next row.**

Type the second new row of data as you did the first. Be sure you press Enter after entering the final data value.

You have updated your worksheet and are ready to continue.

Saving Data

It is a good idea to save the worksheet into a permanent file whenever you make any changes you intend to keep. To save the PULSE worksheet as NEWPULSE (so you don't change the contents of the original worksheet):

Choose File ➤ Save Worksheet As.

Microsoft Windows/DOS: Type NEWPULSE **in the File Name text box, be sure the directory you want is selected, and then click OK.**

Macintosh: Type NEWPULSE **in the Save Worksheet As text box, be sure the folder you want is selected, and then click Save.**

You've created a new file, NEWPULSE.MTW, and this is now your active, open worksheet. The one you originally opened, PULSE.MTW, remains unchanged. Minitab automatically adds the extension .MTW to every file saved with the Save Worksheet As command.

Getting On-Line Help from Minitab

You want to look at some basic statistics for the resting pulse variable, but you're not sure which command to use. When you're not sure how to do something in Minitab, use on-line Help. You decide to look up the phrase "descriptive statistics," using the Search capability. If you are using Minitab for Macintosh Release 8, or Minitab for DOS, see page 2-8 for more information about the structure of Release 8 on-line Help.

Microsoft Windows: Choose Help ➤ Contents.

Macintosh: Drag down on the Help menu ? in the upper-right corner of your screen until your pointer is on Minitab Help, then release the mouse button.

The MINITAB Help Contents window appears.

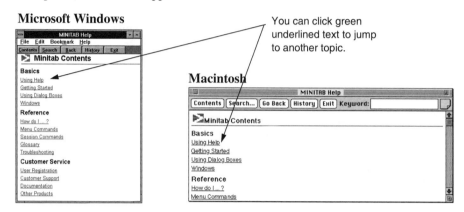

Click the "Search" button at the top of the window. (In Microsoft Windows, if you like, you can go directly to the Search dialog box by choosing **Help ➤ Search for Help on.**)

Microsoft Windows: Type `Descriptive Statistics` in the active text box and then click Show Topics.

Macintosh: Scroll down the Index window until you see the keyword "Descriptive Statistics (Stat menu) on the left hand side. Then scroll through the associated topics on the right until you see the topic "Descriptive Statistics (Stat menu).

Your Search dialog box should look like this

Microsoft Windows: Double-click the Descriptive Statistics (Stat menu) topic in the lower list box.

Macintosh: Double-click the topic "Descriptive Statistics (Stat menu)."

The MINITAB Help window opens to information on the Descriptive Statistics command. The information Minitab displays tells you that this may be the command you need.

Click the first segment of underlined text in the topic "Comparing the Tabular and Graphical Forms of Descriptive Statistics." The MINITAB Help window now displays a new topic, which lists the statistics provided with the Descriptive Statistics command. This is exactly the information you're looking for.

Click the "Exit" button to close the MINITAB window. You return to the Minitab window.

Basic Descriptive Statistics

To describe resting pulses by activity level:

Choose Stat ► Basic Statistics ► Descriptive Statistics. The Descriptive Statistics dialog box opens.

Double-click PULSE1 to place it in the Variables box. This tells Minitab to provide descriptive statistics on the PULSE1 variable.

Click the By variable check box, click the corresponding text box, then double-click ACTIVITY. Your dialog box should look like this:

Click OK. The results appear in the Session window. Choose **Window ➤ Session** (DOS 8, press Alt+M) if you can't see the Session window.

	ACTIVITY	N	MEAN	MEDIAN	TRMEAN	STDEV	SEMEAN
PULSE1	1	9	79.56	82.00	79.56	10.48	3.49
	2	62	72.74	70.00	72.36	10.89	1.38
	3	22	71.59	71.00	71.25	9.39	2.00
	*	1	58.000	58.000	58.000	*	*

	ACTIVITY	MIN	MAX	Q1	Q3
PULSE1	1	62.00	90.00	70.00	90.00
	2	54.00	100.00	65.50	80.00
	3	58.00	92.00	63.50	76.50
	*	58.000	58.000	*	*

When you examine the output it does not surprise you; it seems to conform to what medical research would predict. Take a look at the column labeled Mean. Those at activity level 1 (slight physical activity) have the highest mean resting pulse: 79.56 beats per minute, while those at the activity level 3 (a lot of activity) have the lowest: 71.59 beats per minute. But subjects who are moderately active (level 2) have a mean resting pulse of 72.74, very near to that of level 3. So while the resting pulse does decrease when activity level rises, is the decrease significant?

Analysis of Variance

Minitab's Oneway command is one method you can use to compare the resting pulses of the three different activity levels.

Choose Stat ➤ ANOVA ➤ Oneway. The Oneway Analysis of Variance dialog box opens.

Double-click PULSE1 as the Response and ACTIVITY as the Factor. Your dialog box should look like this:

Click OK. The output appears in the Session window.

```
ANALYSIS OF VARIANCE ON PULSE1
SOURCE      DF        SS        MS        F         p
ACTIVITY     2       433       217     1.95     0.148
ERROR       90      9971       111
TOTAL       92     10404

                              INDIVIDUAL 95 PCT CI'S FOR MEAN
                              BASED ON POOLED STDEV
   LEVEL      N      MEAN     STDEV  ---------+---------+---------+-------
       1      9     79.56     10.48              (-----------*----------)
       2     62     72.74     10.89        (---*----)
       3     22     71.59      9.39  (------*-------)
                                     ---------+---------+---------+-------
POOLED STDEV =     10.53              72.0      78.0      84.0
```

Minitab displays an analysis of variance table and 95% confidence intervals. Because the p-value of .148, reported in the first line of output, is greater than the commonly-used α value of .05, you see no evidence to suggest that there is a significant difference among mean resting pulse rates for different levels of activity.

There could be many reasons for the lack of convincing evidence. When the students originally classified themselves as being very active, moderately active, or only slightly active, they may not have known what criteria to use to judge. If you decide to pursue this subject, you may want to collect more specific data on physical activity, like average number of hours spent exercising each day, types of exercise, and so on.

Boxplots

You may not have accounted for other possible causes of variability, like gender, so exploring that might be a good next step. So far you have been examining the relationship between resting pulse and activity level. Now try looking graphically at resting pulse and gender using the **Graph ➤ Boxplot** command. Do males and females have differing resting pulses?

Choose Graph ➤ Boxplot. The Boxplot dialog box opens.

Double-click PULSE1 as the Y (measurement) and SEX as the X (category) entries. Your dialog box should look like this:

Click OK. The boxplot appears in a separate Graph window.

It appears that males (1) have a lower median resting pulse than females (2).

T-Tests

You can use a two-sample t-test to test the difference in mean resting pulse rates between genders to help you evaluate whether it is statistically significant.

Choose Stat ➤ Basic Statistics ➤ 2-Sample t. The 2-Sample t dialog box opens.

Double-click PULSE1 to place it in the Samples text box and SEX to place it in the Subscripts text box. Your dialog box should look like this:

Click OK. Minitab displays the output in the Session window.

```
TWOSAMPLE T FOR PULSE1
SEX   N     MEAN    STDEV    SE MEAN
1     59    70.66   9.47     1.2
2     35    76.9    11.6     2.0

95 PCT CI FOR MU 1 - MU 2: (-10.8, -1.6)

TTEST MU 1 = MU 2 (VS NE): T = -2.67   P = 0.0097   DF = 60
```

The mean resting pulse for males (1) is 70.66 beats per minute, while for females (2) it is 76.9 beats per minute. The p-value of .0097, which is smaller than the commonly-used α value of .05, suggests that there may be a significant difference in mean resting pulse rates between males and females.

Manipulating Columns

Is the difference in pulse rates before and after running also lower in men than in women? You decide to examine the change in the students' first and second pulse readings for those who ran in place. Start by creating columns that will contain data only for the runners.

Creating New Columns

First create a column that stores the difference in all pulses; that is, PULSE2 – PULSE1. Call the column DIFF.

Choose Calc ➤ Mathematical Expressions. The Mathematical Expressions dialog box opens.

Type DIFF in the Variable (new or modified) text box, then press Tab twice.

Type 'PULSE2' - 'PULSE1' in the Expression text box. Your dialog box should look like this:

Click OK. You could check the Data window to see the new column, C9.

Creating Column Subsets

Now create two new columns, DIFFRAN and SEXRAN, that contain the pulse differences for those who ran in place and their genders. Use the **Copy Columns** command to tell Minitab to find the data for only those who ran and to copy it from DIFF into DIFFRAN and SEX into SEXRAN, and then check the Info window to get a count. (In the RAN column, 1 = ran in place while 2 = did not run in place.)

Choose Manip ► Copy Columns (Release 8 **Calc ► Copy Columns**).

Type DIFF SEX in the Copy from columns box and press [Tab].

Type DIFFRAN SEXRAN in the To columns box:

Click Use Rows. The Copy - Use Rows dialog box opens.

Click Use rows with column, click the corresponding text box, double-click RAN, then type 1 in the equal to text box. The Copy - Use Rows dialog box should look like this:

Click OK in both dialog boxes.

Choose Window ➤ Info (DOS 8 type INFO in the Session window) to see the counts of DIFF and SEX:

Out of 94 students, only 36 got heads when they flipped their coins, so only 36 ran in place.

Comparing Levels of a Variable

Now that C10 DIFFRAN contains the pulse difference for those who ran in place, and C11 SEXRAN contains the genders of those students, take a graphical look at how gender might affect the pulse difference. Create a boxplot of DIFFRAN by gender.

Choose Graph ➤ Boxplot.

Double-click DIFFRAN as the Y (measurement) variable and SEXRAN as the X (category) variable, and then click OK. The graph appears in its own Graph window.

Minitab displays the boxplot, including two outliers (indicated by asterisks). It appears that everyone's pulse increased after having run in place for one minute, but in general the males (1) did not experience as great an increase as the females (2). Test this difference in mean pulse increase using a two-sample t-test.

Choose Stat ➤ Basic Statistics ➤ 2-Sample t.

Click the Samples text box, double-click DIFFRAN, double-click SEXRAN, and then click OK. The output appears in the Session window.

```
TWOSAMPLE T FOR DIFFRAN
SEXRAN    N      MEAN     STDEV    SE MEAN
1        25      12.9     12.2       2.4
2        11      31.9     11.9       3.6

95 PCT CI FOR MU 1 - MU 2: (-28.1, -9.9)
TTEST MU 1 = MU 2 (VS NE): T = -4.38  P = 0.0003  DF = 19
```

The mean pulse increase for males after running in place for one minute is 12.9 beats per minute, while for females it is 31.9. The p-value of .0003 suggests that this difference is significant.

Scatter Plots

Might you be able to predict a runner's post-running pulse (C2 PULSE2) based on his or her resting pulse rate (C1 PULSE1)? To test this, you'll create two new columns, P1RAN and P2RAN, that contain the resting pulse and post-running pulses for just the runners. Use **Manip ➤ Copy Columns** to copy the pulse information from C1 and C2, using only the data of those who ran in place for one minute (coded by RAN = 1). (You can refer to columns by either number or name.)

Choose Manip ➤ Copy Columns (Release 8, Calc ➤ Copy Columns).

Type C1 C2 into the Copy from columns text box, replacing what is there, press Tab**, and then type P1RAN P2RAN.**

Click Use Rows and verify that the settings still show using RAN equal to 1.

Click OK twice.

Take a look at a scatter plot of the runners' post-running pulse readings (P2RAN) vs. their resting pulse readings (P1RAN) to get a feel for the relationship between these two variables.

Choose Graph ➤ Plot.

Double-click P2RAN as the Y variable and P1RAN as the X variable, and then click OK. The graph appears in its own Graph window.

It does seem that, on the average, post-running pulse rate increases as resting pulse rate increases.

Plotting a Fitted Regression Line (Release 10)

The Fitted Line Plot command can help you predict post-running pulse from resting pulse readings. Tell Minitab the variable you want to predict (post-running pulse, or P2RAN) and the variable you want as a predictor (resting pulse, or P1RAN).

Choose Stat ➤ Regression ➤ Fitted Line Plot.

Double-click P2RAN as the Response variable and P1RAN as the Predictor variable.

Click OK.

Minitab generates the following high-resolution graph:

The regression equation, P2RAN = 18.2 + 1.01 P1RAN (y is P2RAN and x is P1RAN), tells you that to predict (approximately) the pulse after running, add 18.2 to the resting pulse. The fitted regression line shows the fitted values plotted along with the actual data. The R-squared value of 36.8% indicates that this model explains less than 40% of the total variability. Since you learned earlier that men and women have different pulse rates, you suspect perhaps you should have included gender in the model to account for some of the additional variability.

Save your worksheet once again.

Choose File ➤ Save Worksheet. This replaces the NEWPULSE file created earlier with the new version of the worksheet.

Saving Your Session

To save your session, the work that appeared in the Session window, you simply activate that window and then use the Save Window As command. Your session is saved as a text file, which you can open in any text editor or word processor. The only part of your session that is not saved is any high-resolution graphs you created (the ones that appeared in separate Graph windows). You'll see how to save those in Chapter 6.

Choose Window ➤ Session.

Choose File ➤ Save Window As.

Type Session in the File Name text box, select the directory you want to use, and then click OK.

There are many directions you could go from here with this data set. An analysis of covariance (using the **Stat ➤ ANOVA ➤ Analysis of Covariance** command; see on-line Help for more information) would take gender into account, and you have not even begun to consider the smoking data, or the weights and heights of the students. But you have seen how a typical Minitab session progresses, and how to use some basic commands. Try some of what you've learned on the rest of the data set; you may uncover some surprises!

When you are done:

Choose File ➤ Exit (or File ➤ Quit for the Macintosh).

This ends your Minitab session. PULSE.MTW is in its original form, NEWPULSE.MTW contains the updated worksheet, and SESSION.TXT contains a record of the entire session (except for the high-resolution graphs you didn't save in separate files). If you want a printout of your session, print the file SESSION.TXT.

Now What?

This sample session and the one in Chapter 2 give you practice using Minitab. The rest of this manual is more of a reference guide than a tutorial. You could start by reading through Chapters 3 and 4 to learn how to use Minitab's worksheet and command structure and the basics of data entry and creating and saving worksheets. From there, you can browse through the rest of the chapters as need arises, using the index to direct you.

You can study the examples that accompany most of the commands in the manual, and duplicate them while running Minitab on your own computer. The best way to learn is by trying it yourself.

2

Sample Session for Command Users

- Starting Minitab
- Saving, retrieving, and viewing data
- Correcting the worksheet by changing and adding data
- Getting on-line Help
- Looking at data graphically with dotplots, box-and-whisker plots, and scatter plots
- Computing basic descriptive statistics
- Performing a statistical analysis, including analysis of variance, t-tests, and plotting a fitted regression line

How to Use the Sample Session

Chapters 1 and 2 are hands-on introductions to Minitab statistical software. Chapter 1 uses the menus and dialog boxes available with recent releases of Minitab while Chapter 2 uses the session commands available in all releases. See page 1-2 for information on releases of Minitab and their command compatibility. If your release supports only session commands, use the Chapter 2 sample session. Otherwise, you can work through the sample session in Chapter 1, and then either skip this chapter or proceed through it if you would like experience working with session commands (it can sometimes be quicker). Both Chapters 1 and 2 use the same data and analysis methods.

In this sample session you assume the role of the data analyst not only to experience a normal Minitab session, but also to learn your way around Minitab. The sample session starts with the basics of opening, exploring, modifying, and saving a worksheet. Later in the session you will try some of Minitab's statistical commands. The commands used in this session are covered in detail in later chapters of this manual.

Getting Started

You will need the Minitab worksheet PULSE.MTW that comes with the sample data in every release of Minitab. If, even after following the directions in this session, you can't find this file, see your System Administrator for help. Read through the description of the PULSE data in the beginning of Chapter 1 before you start this session.

In the beginning, the instructions will tell you to type certain commands, like this: **Type MINITAB**. After you get started, you will simply type what you see after Minitab's various prompts. Press Enter (or Return on some keyboards) after every line you type (the instructions will remind you of this at first). Although this manual shows all commands in capital letters, you can use any combination of upper- and lowercase letters. If you make a mistake while typing a command, backspace over it and retype it. If you have already pressed Enter, retype the command on a new command line. If you find slight discrepancies between what you see on your screen and the output shown throughout the sample session, don't worry. We are probably just using different versions of Minitab.

Starting Minitab

Begin by starting Minitab:

Type MINITAB after your computer's prompt and press Enter (or Return on some keyboards).

If you have trouble starting Minitab, ask your System Administrator for help. The opening screen displays information about Minitab, followed by the prompt MTB>. This prompt is Minitab's way of telling you that it is waiting for you to enter a command.

```
MINITAB Statistical Software Release 9.1
(C) Copyright 1992 Minitab Inc. - ALL RIGHTS RESERVED
July 1, 1995
Storage Available: 100000

MTB >
```

If your version of Minitab uses windows, choose the session command from the Window menu to activate the Session window and find the MTB> prompt. Your opening screen may differ, depending on the Minitab release and computer platform you are using.

Saving Your Session in a File

Minitab does not save your work unless you tell it to, so it is a good practice to begin by creating a file that stores a record of the entire session. Type the following line after the MTB> prompt. Always press the Enter (or Return) key at the end of any line you type.

Type OUTFILE 'SESSION' and press Enter.

The command you type appears on the screen:

```
MTB > OUTFILE 'SESSION'
```

From this point on, Minitab stores a record of your session in an *outfile*, a text or ASCII file, named SESSION. Minitab automatically adds the file extension .LIS (as in *listing*) to the name to identify its file type. You can open this file later in a text editor or print it for a record of your session.

Retrieving Data from a File

Now retrieve the Minitab saved worksheet named PULSE.MTW. Different systems require different retrieval instructions. You will use the RETRIEVE command and the path name that gives the location of PULSE.MTW on your system. If your system isn't mentioned in the following chart, see your System Administrator.

System	Path Name
VAX/VMS	'MTBDIR:PULSE'
Sun/SunOS™	'/usr/local/lib/minitab/handbook/pulse'
IBM VM/CMS®	'PULSE'
HP®9000 (Unix)	'/usr/local/minitab/sav/pulse'
Microsoft Windows	'c:\mtbwin\data\pulse'
Macintosh	'pulse'

Type RETRIEVE and the path name for your system.

On a VAX, this looks like:

```
MTB > RETRIEVE  'SYS$MINITAB:PULSE'
 WORKSHEET SAVED 10/18/1991

Worksheet retrieved from file: SYS$MINITAB\PULSE.MTW
```

Always enclose a file name with single quotation marks. If you have trouble retrieving the PULSE.MTW worksheet, ask someone familiar with the Minitab installation at your site to tell you where the sample data sets are installed on your system. Then type the RETRIEVE command as shown, substituting the correct path information.

Viewing Data

To remind yourself of what the data set contains, obtain a listing of all the variables in the current worksheet. The INFO command displays a summary that lists column numbers, column names, and the number of rows in each column.

From now on, the instructions will show just the Minitab prompts and the commands. So for this next instruction, you would simply type the word **INFO** and press (Enter). The output that follows the command line should match what you see on your screen (except, of course, because of slight differences across releases and platforms).

```
MTB > INFO

COLUMN    NAME      COUNT
C1        PULSE1      92
C2        PULSE2      92
C3        RAN         92
C4        SMOKES      92
C5        SEX         92
C6        HEIGHT      92
C7        WEIGHT      92
C8        ACTIVITY    92

CONSTANTS USED: NONE
```

This displays each column's name and the number of individual observations it contains. Now look at a listing of individual values in the worksheet, using the PRINT command (typing C1-C8 is easier than typing C1 C2 C3 C4 C5 C6 C7 C8, though Minitab accepts either method).

```
MTB > PRINT C1-C8
```

ROW	PULSE1	PULSE2	RAN	SMOKES	SEX	HEIGHT	WEIGHT	ACTIVITY
1	64	88	1	2	1	66.00	140	2
2	58	70	1	2	1	72.00	145	2
3	62	76	1	1	1	73.50	160	3
4	66	78	1	1	1	73.00	190	1
5	64	80	1	2	1	69.00	155	2
6	74	84	1	2	1	73.00	165	1
7	84	84	1	2	1	72.00	150	3
8	68	72	1	2	1	74.00	190	2
9	62	75	1	2	1	72.00	195	2
10	76	118	1	2	1	71.00	138	2
11	90	94	1	1	1	74.00	160	1
12	80	96	1	2	1	72.00	155	2
13	92	84	1	1	1	70.00	153	3
14	68	76	1	2	1	67.00	145	2
15	60	76	1	2	1	71.00	170	3
16	62	58	1	2	1	72.00	175	3
17	66	82	1	1	1	69.00	175	2
18	70	72	1	1	1	73.00	170	3
19	68	76	1	1	1	74.00	180	2

After printing as much data as the screen can display, Minitab might ask if you want to view more. Since all you wanted was a glance over the data:

```
Continue? N
```

Some users prefer not to be interrupted by Continue? prompts. If you want to suppress this prompt, type OH 0 (that is, output height = 0) after the MTB> prompt. On Microsoft Windows, Macintosh, and later MS-DOS releases, you can scroll through the Session window to see your output. To restore the Continue? prompt, type OH 24.

Starting Your Analysis

You could analyze this data set in a number of ways. You decide to start by examining C1 PULSE1, the variable containing the first pulse reading (that is, resting pulse). Is there any variation, perhaps by activity level? Previous medical research suggests that the more active people are, the lower their resting pulses are. Is this true for your class?

Looking at a Dotplot

Most statisticians feel that it is good statistical practice to begin analysis by looking at the data graphically. You decide to look at the distribution of the students' resting pulses by activity level using a dotplot, using the DOTPLOT command with the subcommand BY. Note that you only have to type the first four letters of any Minitab command. The rest of this Sample session will use that shortcut from time to time. Be sure to type the punctuation correctly. The ; tells Minitab that a subcommand will follow, and the . tells Minitab that you are done typing the command. When you type the ; the MTB> prompt changes to SUBC>. The prompt MTB> says, "I'm ready for a command," while SUBC> says, "I'll accept subcommands until you tell me to stop by typing a period."

```
MTB > DOTP 'PULSE1';
SUBC>   BY 'ACTIVITY'.

ACTIVITY
0             .
        ---+---------+---------+---------+---------+---------+---PULSE1
ACTIVITY
1                                              .
              .   .      .    .  . .      :
        ---+---------+---------+---------+---------+---------+---PULSE1
                        :
ACTIVITY            .    : .
2              . :   : : : :  . . . .        .
           : : :.: : : : : : : : : : :   : . . . :    .
        ---+---------+---------+---------+---------+---------+---PULSE1
ACTIVITY        .     .
3              . . : :   : . : . : .    . ..     .
        ---+---------+---------+---------+---------+---------+---PULSE1
          50        60        70        80        90       100
```

The dotplots don't offer much conclusive evidence, although you can see that most of the students classified their activity level as "moderate," or activity level 2. Recall that level 1 is "slight" and 3 is "a lot" of physical activity. All three groups have resting pulse readings that range quite a bit.

Correcting the Worksheet

But what is activity level 0, the first dotplot? Checking back at the data set description, you notice that there shouldn't be a level 0. Moreover, it corresponds with a resting pulse of 48, a rather low reading. The person entering the data could have made a few mistakes—easy enough to do, and something that statisticians must always watch for. The entry of 0 could have a significant effect on your subsequent analysis.

Making Global Changes Using CODE

You decide to delete the 0 activity level and replace it with the missing value symbol, an asterisk (*), since you're not sure what it should be. One way to change the 0 to * is by using the CODE command. Tell

Minitab to replace every 0 it finds in the column ACTIVITY with the symbol ∗, and put it back in the same column.

```
MTB > CODE (0) '*' 'ACTIVITY' 'ACTIVITY'
```

To verify that Minitab has changed the 0 to a ∗, use the INFO command once more, getting information only on C8 ACTIVITY:

```
MTB > INFO C8
COLUMN     NAME      COUNT   MISSING
C8         ACTIVITY    92       1

CONSTANTS USED: NONE
```

Minitab now reports one missing value in C8. It looks like you've taken care of the problem.

Changing Individual Worksheet Values Using LET

You still need to decide how to handle the surprisingly low resting pulse entry of 48 that corresponded to the 0 activity level. Leafing back through the survey sheets the students turned in, you are able to find the sheet corresponding with this person (luckily the person entering the data kept the pile of record sheets in order). There you find that student failed to enter an activity level (which may be why it was entered as 0), and that the resting pulse should have been 58, not 48. To fix this mistake, found in row 54 of the data set, use the LET command.

To tell Minitab to let the value in C1, row 54, be equal to 58 instead of 48:

```
MTB > LET C1(54) = 58
```

You could repeat the DOTPLOT command if you want to take another look at the data set with the corrections made.

Inserting Data

Just as you think you have the worksheet all tidied up, your professor informs you that two students who missed class the day of the experiment want their data included. The INFO command told you that there are presently 92 rows in the worksheet, so add the two new cases in rows 93 and 94. The two students report the following data:

PULSE1	PULSE2	RAN	SMOKES	SEX	HEIGHT	WEIGHT	ACTIVITY
73	84	1	2	1	65	138	2
72	70	2	2	1	72	185	3

The INSERT command lets you enter new rows of data in columns that already contain data. First tell Minitab into which columns you want to enter the data, then type the data after the DATA> prompt, and finally, tell Minitab when to end reading data:

```
MTB > INSERT C1-C8
DATA>    73 84 1 2 1 65 138 2
DATA>    72 70 2 2 1 72 185 3
DATA> END
        2 ROWS READ
```

Minitab tells you that it has read two new rows. You have updated your worksheet and are ready to continue.

Saving Data

It is a good idea to save the worksheet into a permanent file whenever you make any changes you intend to keep. To save the PULSE worksheet as NEWPULSE (so you don't change the contents of the original worksheet):

```
MTB > SAVE 'NEWPULSE'
  Worksheet saved into file: NEWPULSE.MTW
```

You've created a new file, NEWPULSE, and this is now your active, open worksheet. The one you originally opened, PULSE.MTW, remains unchanged. Minitab automatically adds the extension .MTW to every file saved with the SAVE command to indicate that it is a binary saved worksheet file.

Getting On-Line Help from Minitab

You want to look at some basic statistics for the resting pulse variable, but you're not sure which command to use. When you're not sure how to do something in Minitab, use the HELP command.

```
MTB > HELP
```

The HELP screen you see depends on the version of Minitab that you are running. If you are using Minitab for Windows Release 9 or 10, or Minitab for Macintosh Release 10, typing HELP takes you to the Minitab Contents screen, a table of contents from which you can jump to other topics. You can also type HELP with any session command to go directly to information on that command. For example:

```
MTB > HELP REGRESS
```

See page 1-9 for more information on Release 9 for Windows and Release 10 Help.

If you are not using Release 9 or 10, continue reading this section.

```
MTB > HELP HELP
```

The HELP HELP screen lists the various categories available to you. Suppose you want to look at some basic descriptive statistics for the resting pulse variable, but are not sure how to do it. You decide to get help on COMMANDS to find out which command to use.

Type N when Minitab asks you if you want more information.

The HELP COMMANDS screen lists all the command categories. The list depends on which release of Minitab you are running.

```
MTB > HELP COMMANDS

To get a list of the Minitab commands in one of the categories
below, type HELP COMMANDS followed by the appropriate number,
(HELP COMMANDS 1, for example).

 1 General Information          11 Tables
 2 Input and Output of Data     12 Time Series
 3 Editing and Manipulating     13 Statistical Process Control
   Data                         14 Exploratory Data Analysis
 4 Arithmetic                   15 Distributions & Random Data
 5 Plotting Data                16 Sorting
 6 Basic Statistics             17 Matrices
 7 Regression                   18 Miscellaneous
 8 Analysis of Variance         19 Stored Commands and Loops
 9 Multivariate Analysis        20 How Commands are Explained
10 Nonparametrics                  in HELP
```

Item 6, Basic Statistics, looks like a good place to start. If you are using Minitab for Macintosh Release 8, just double-click the topic you want to see. Otherwise, type:

```
MTB > HELP COMMANDS 6
```

The information Minitab displays tells you that DESCRIBE may be the command you need. Now get help on that specific command:

```
MTB > HELP DESCRIBE
```

Minitab offers a wide array of basic statistics to help you analyze your data, and this HELP screen lists them. The DESCRIBE command provides exactly the information you're looking for, and the BY subcommand gives you the opportunity to produce separate summary statistics for the resting pulses of students at each activity level.

Basic Descriptive Statistics

To describe resting pulses by activity level (you only need to type the first four letters of any command):

```
MTB > DESC 'PULSE1';
SUBC>   BY 'ACTIVITY'.

        ACTIVITY       N      MEAN    MEDIAN    TRMEAN    STDEV   SEMEAN
PULSE1         1       9     79.56     82.00     79.56    10.48     3.49
               2      62     72.74     70.00     72.36    10.89     1.38
               3      22     71.59     71.00     71.25     9.39     2.00
               *       1    58.000    58.000    58.000        *        *

        ACTIVITY     MIN       MAX        Q1        Q3
PULSE1         1   62.00     90.00     70.00     90.00
               2   54.00    100.00     65.50     80.00
               3   58.00     92.00     63.50     76.50
               *  58.000    58.000         *         *
```

When you examine the output it does not surprise you; it seems to conform to what medical research would predict. Take a look at the column labeled MEAN. Those at activity level 1 (slight physical activity) have the highest mean resting pulse: 79.56 beats per minute, while those at the activity level 3 (a lot of activity) have the lowest: 71.59 beats per minute. But subjects who are moderately active (level 2) have a mean resting pulse of 72.74, very near to that of level 3. So while the resting pulse does decrease when activity level rises, is the decrease significant?

Analysis of Variance

Minitab's ONEWAY command is one method you can use to compare the resting pulses of the three different activity levels.

```
MTB > ONEW 'PULSE1' 'ACTIVITY'

ANALYSIS OF VARIANCE ON PULSE1
SOURCE      DF        SS        MS       F        p
ACTIVITY     2       433       217    1.95    0.148
ERROR       90      9971       111
TOTAL       92     10404

                              INDIVIDUAL 95 PCT CI'S FOR MEAN
                              BASED ON POOLED STDEV
  LEVEL      N      MEAN     STDEV  ---------+---------+---------+-------
      1      9     79.56     10.48               (-----------*----------)
      2     62     72.74     10.89         (---*----)
      3     22     71.59      9.39     (------*-------)
                                      ---------+---------+---------+-------
POOLED STDEV =     10.53               72.0      78.0      84.0
```

Minitab displays an analysis of variance table and 95% confidence intervals. Because the p-value of .148, reported in the first line of output, is greater than the commonly-used α value of .05, you see no evidence to suggest that there is a significant difference among mean resting pulse rates for different levels of activity.

There could be many reasons for the lack of convincing evidence. When the students originally classified themselves as being very active, moderately active, or only slightly active, they may not have known what criteria to use to judge. If you decide to pursue this subject, you may want to collect more specific data on physical activity, like average number of hours spent exercising each day, types of exercise, and so on.

Boxplots

You may not have accounted for other possible causes of variability, like gender, so exploring that might be a good next step. Up until now you have been examining the relationship between resting pulse and activity level.

The syntax for high-resolution graphics commands changes in Release 9 Enhanced for VAX/VMS, Release 9 for Windows and later versions. To keep things simple during this session, we will continue to use character graphics. To make sure you are in character graphics mode, type the following in Release 9 Enhanced for VAX/VMS, Release 9 for Windows and later versions (if you are not sure what release you have, type this command anyway).

```
MTB > GSTD
```

With Release 9 Enhanced for VAX/VMS, Release 9 for Windows and later versions, you should get the following output:

```
* NOTE  * Standard Graphics are enabled.
          Professional Graphics are disabled.
          Use the GPRO command to enable Professional Graphics.
```

If you typed GSTD and got an error message (such as ERROR Name not found in dictionary), this means you can use character graphics and possibly the older, G-style high-resolution graphics. You can read more about the different graphics types in Chapter 6, and in the Quick Reference in Appendix A.

Now try looking graphically at resting pulse and gender using the BOXPLOT command. Do males and females have differing resting pulses? Type the following:

```
MTB > BOXP 'PULSE1';
SUBC>   BY 'SEX'.

SEX
                             -----------
   1         *       ----------I    +    I-------------- * *
                             -----------

                         -------------------
   2              ---------I          +         I--------------
                         -------------------
         ----+---------+---------+---------+---------+---------+--PULSE1
            50        60        70        80        90       100
```

It appears that males (1) have a lower median resting pulse than females (2).

T-Tests

You can use a two-sample t-test to test the difference in mean resting pulse rates between genders to help you evaluate whether the difference is statistically significant.

```
MTB > TWOT 'PULSE1' 'SEX'

TWOSAMPLE T FOR PULSE1
SEX   N     MEAN    STDEV   SE MEAN
1    59    70.66    9.47      1.2
2    35    76.9     11.6      2.0

95 PCT CI FOR MU 1 - MU 2: (-10.8, -1.6)

TTEST MU 1 = MU 2 (VS NE): T = -2.67   P = 0.0097   DF = 60
```

The mean resting pulse for males (1) is 70.66 beats per minute, while for females (2) it is 76.9 beats per minute. The p-value of .0097, which is smaller than the commonly-used α value of .05, suggests that there may be a significant difference in mean resting pulse rates between males and females.

Manipulating Columns

Is the difference in pulse rates before and after running also lower in men than in women? You decide to examine the change in the students' first and second pulse readings for those who ran in place. Start by creating columns that will contain data only for the runners.

Creating New Columns Using LET

First create a column that stores the difference in all pulses; that is, PULSE2 – PULSE1. Call the column DIFF. Minitab's NAME and LET commands make this easy.

```
MTB > NAME C9 'DIFF'
MTB > LET 'DIFF' = 'PULSE2' - 'PULSE1'
```

Creating Column Subsets Using COPY

Now create two new columns, DIFFRAN and SEXRAN, that contain the pulse differences for those who ran in place and their genders. Use the COPY command to tell Minitab to find the data for only those who ran and to copy it from DIFF into DIFFRAN and from SEX into SEXRAN, and then use INFO to get a count. (In the RAN column, 1 = ran in place while 2 = did not run in place.)

```
MTB > NAME C10 'DIFFRAN' C11 'SEXRAN'
MTB > COPY 'DIFF' 'SEX' 'DIFFRAN' 'SEXRAN';
SUBC>    USE 'RAN' = 1.
```

Take a look at the columns you just created.

```
MTB > INFO C9-C11

COLUMN    NAME      COUNT
C9        DIFF        94
C10       DIFFRAN     36
C11       SEXRAN      36
```

Out of 94 students, only 36 got heads when they flipped their coins, so only 36 ran in place.

Comparing Levels of a Variable

Now that C10 DIFFRAN contains the pulse difference for those who ran in place, and C11 SEXRAN contains the genders of those students, take a graphical look at how gender might affect the pulse difference. Create a boxplot of DIFFRAN by gender.

```
MTB > BOXP 'DIFFRAN';
SUBC>   BY 'SEXRAN'.
```

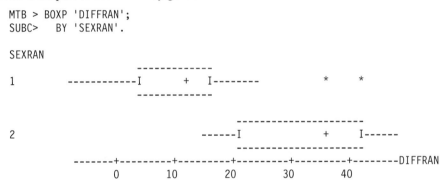

Minitab displays the boxplot, including two outliers (indicated by asterisks). It appears that everyone's pulse increased after having run in place for one minute, but in general the males (1) did not experience as great an increase as the females (2). Test this difference in mean pulse increase using a two-sample t-test.

```
MTB > TWOT 'DIFFRAN' 'SEXRAN'

TWOSAMPLE T FOR DIFFRAN
SEXRAN    N      MEAN    STDEV   SE MEAN
1         25     12.9    12.2      2.4
2         11     31.9    11.9      3.6

95 PCT CI FOR MU 1 - MU 2: (-28.1, -9.9)
TTEST MU 1 = MU 2 (VS NE): T = -4.38  P = 0.0003  DF = 19
```

The mean pulse increase for males after running in place for one minute is 12.9 beats per minute, while for females it is 31.9. The p-value of .0003 suggests that this difference may be significant.

Scatter Plots

Might you be able to predict a runner's post-running pulse (C2 PULSE2) based on his or her resting pulse rate (C1 PULSE1)? To test this, you'll create two new columns, P1RAN and P2RAN, that contain the resting pulse and post-running pulses for just the runners. First, name C12 and C13 with these new column names, and then copy the pulse information from C1 and C2, using only the data of those who ran in place for one minute (coded by RAN = 1). (You can refer to columns by either number or name.)

```
MTB > NAME C12 'P1RAN' C13 'P2RAN'
MTB > COPY C1 C2 C12 C13;
SUBC>   USE 'RAN' = 1.
```

Take a look at a scatter plot of the runners' post-running pulse readings (P2RAN) vs. their resting pulse readings (P1RAN) to get a feel for the relationship between these two variables.

```
MTB > PLOT 'P2RAN' 'P1RAN'
```

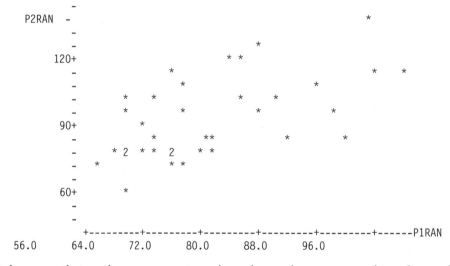

It does seem that, on the average, post-running pulse rate increases as resting pulse rate increases.

Plotting a Fitted Regression Line (optional)

The %FITLINE command, available in Release 9 Enhanced for VAX/VMS, Release 9 for Windows and later versions, can help you predict post-running pulse from resting pulse readings (the % before the command indicates that it is a macro; on-line Help can tell you more). If your version of Minitab doesn't support this command, you can get the same information using the REGRESS command and can then create a scatter plot. Tell Minitab the variable you want to predict (post-running pulse, or P2RAN) and the variable you want as a predictor (resting pulse, or P1RAN). Use the GPRO command first to enable high-resolution graphics.

```
MTB > GPRO
MTB > %FITLINE 'P2RAN' 'P1RAN'
```

Minitab generates the following high-resolution graph:

The regression equation, P2RAN = 18.2 + 1.01 P1RAN (y is P2RAN and x is P1RAN), tells you that to predict (approximately) the pulse after running, add 18.2 to the resting pulse. The fitted regression line shows the fitted values plotted along with the actual data. The R-squared value of 36.8% indicates that this model explains less than 40% of the total variability. Since you learned earlier that men and women have different pulse rates, you suspect perhaps you should have included gender in the model to account for some of the additional variability.

Finishing Your Session

Now you need to return to the MTB> prompt. How you do this depends on your version of Minitab and your computer platform. For Windows and Macintosh versions, choose **Window ➤ Session** at this point. Save your worksheet once again.

```
MTB > SAVE 'NEWPULSE'

Worksheet saved into file: NEWPULSE.MTW
```

If you are asked if you want to replace the old worksheet, type Y. This replaces the NEWPULSE file created earlier with the new version of the worksheet.

This is a good time to take a break. Remember that you began the session by opening an outfile called SESSION.LIS. Minitab has been saving all the steps you took in your analysis in this file.

Type NOOUTFILE to end the file SESSION.LIS.

There are many directions you could go from here with this data set. An analysis of covariance (using the ANCOVA command; see Appendix A for its syntax and on-line Help for more information) would take gender into account, and you have not even begun to consider the smoking data, or the weights and heights of the students. But you have seen how a typical Minitab session progresses, and how to use some basic commands. Try some of what you've learned on the rest of the data set; you may uncover some surprises!

When you are done:

Type STOP.

On Microsoft Windows and Macintosh versions, you might receive a prompt to save your session results. You can click No to discard the results.

This ends your Minitab session. PULSE.MTW is in its original form, NEWPULSE.MTW contains the updated worksheet, and SESSION.LIS contains a record of the entire session (except for the fitted regression line plot, which is high-resolution and therefore can't be saved in an outfile; high-resolution graphic must be printed seperately). If you want a printout of your session, print the file SESSION.LIS. You could print the fitted regression line plot as well; see Chapter 4 for information on printing.

Now What?

This sample session has given you practice using Minitab. The rest of this manual is more of a reference guide than a tutorial. Chapters 3 and 4 show how to use Minitab's worksheet and command structure and the basics of data entry and creating and saving worksheets. Chapter 5 shows how the basics of editing and manipulating data in Minitab. Chapter 6 provides more details on Minitab graphics capabilities.

You can study the examples that accompany most of the commands in the manual, and duplicate the examples using Minitab on your own computer.

3

Overview of Minitab

- Start Minitab
- Exit (STOP)
- Menus and dialog boxes
- Minitab windows
- The Minitab worksheet
- Session commands
- Help (HELP)
- Alpha and numeric data
- Minitab symbols and prompts

Minitab is a statistical tool designed to help you analyze data efficiently and effectively. This chapter introduces you to the main parts of Minitab and gets you started using some basic Minitab commands. There are about 200 commands for entering data into a worksheet, manipulating and transforming data, producing graphical and numerical summaries, and performing a wide range of statistical analyses.

Although the sample sessions in Chapters 1 and 2 were for menu users and session command users, respectively, from this point on, instructions are combined for all users. Be sure you understand which version of Minitab you are using and what operating system you are using. Within the variation of versions and operating systems, there are two general classes of Minitab users.

1. **Session command users:** This group of users is most likely using an operating system like DOS, UNIX, or VAX/VMS. When you first start your computer, you will often see a system prompt, like C:\> or % or $ on the lower-left of your screen. The system prompt is waiting for you to type a command that tells the computer what you want it to do. If you are a session command user, you should look for the instructions for session command users and ignore the ones for menu users.

2. **Menu and Dialog Box users:** This group of users is most likely using a Macintosh or a PC running Microsoft Windows. When you first start your computer, you will often see a screen with icons (small pictures) and menus, as shown here for Microsoft Windows. In this environment, you tell the computer what you want to do by selecting commands from menus, often by using a pointing device such as a mouse or track ball. If you are a menu user, you should look for the instructions for menu users and ignore the ones for session command users (although all menu versions of Minitab still allow session commands, and you might prefer using session commands over menus).

Note that some operating systems allow the use of shells that might make you think your version of Minitab supports menus when it really doesn't. Likewise, some versions of Minitab offer basic menu capabilities to operating systems that don't support the full range of menu and dialog box options described in this book. If you aren't sure where your version of Minitab or your operating system fits in, see your System Administrator for guidance.

Starting and Stopping Minitab

Starting Minitab. How you start Minitab depends on your operating system. If you are running DOS, UNIX, or VAX/VMS, you usually type MINITAB after the prompt, and then press ⌐Enter⌐ (or ⌐Return⌐ on some keyboards). The MTB> prompt appears, ready for you to enter commands. (See *Session Commands* on page 3-8 for more information.) If you are using a Macintosh or a PC running Microsoft Windows, you locate and open the Minitab program group or folder, and then double-click the Minitab icon, which looks similar to this:

Minitab 10.5
Xtra

When Minitab is started for the first time, the main Minitab window opens as shown (if you have changed the configuration of your windows they may appear differently):

Stopping Minitab. If you are using session commands you type STOP after the MTB> prompt and then press ⌐Enter⌐. Using the menus, choose **File ➤ Exit** (**File ➤ Quit** for the Macintosh).

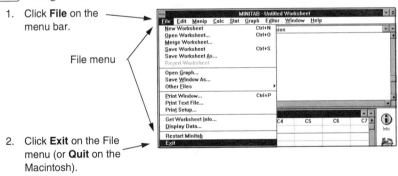

1. Click **File** on the menu bar.

   File menu

2. Click **Exit** on the File menu (or **Quit** on the Macintosh).

Menus and Dialog Boxes

Be sure you understand which version of Minitab you are using and what operating system your computer is using, as described in the beginning of this chapter. You may or may not have access to Minitab commands using menus and dialog boxes. When you start Minitab and you see only the MTB> prompt, the Minitab menus are probably not available to you. When menus and dialog boxes are not available to you, you do your work using session commands (see *Session Commands* on page 3-8). If you have started Minitab and you see a bar across the top with menu names like File and Edit, then you can issue Minitab commands using menus.

Working with Menus

The horizontal bar across the top of the screen is the *menu bar*. It contains Minitab's main menus: File, Edit, Manip, Calc, Stat, Graph, Editor, and Window. In Microsoft Windows, the menu bar also contains the Help menu, while on the Macintosh, Help is accessed through the balloon on the upper-right corner of the screen. Each menu contains a set of Minitab commands.

Using a Mouse. There are four basic mouse operations:

Pointing	To point to an item, move the mouse so that the mouse cursor is on that item.
Clicking	To click an item, point to the item, and then, without moving the mouse, press and release the mouse button.
Double-clicking	To double-click an item, point to the item, and then press the mouse button twice in rapid succession without moving the mouse.
Dragging	To drag an item, point to the item, press down and hold the mouse button, move the mouse pointer and item to another location, and then release the mouse button.

You open a menu by clicking the menu name. To choose a command, click the menu name, then drag down until the pointer is on the command you want. Then release the mouse button to choose the highlighted command. To close a menu or submenu without making a choice, move the mouse pointer off the menu and release the mouse button.

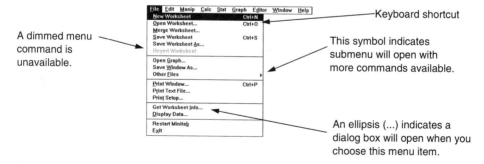

Working with Dialog Boxes

When you choose a menu command followed by an ellipsis (such as with Open Worksheet in the previous figure), a dialog box opens that lets you select variables and other options. This example uses the Cross Tabulation dialog box (**Stat ➤ Tables ➤ Cross Tabulation**) to show how you use a typical dialog box.

This list box shows available columns; double-click the ones you want in the active text box (the one containing the cursor).

Text boxes display columns or options you enter; this text box allows more than one column.

Click check boxes to include or exclude certain features.

Click an option button to choose from among mutually-exclusive options.

Clicking a button followed by an ellipsis (...) displays another dialog box with other options.

This text box accepts a single column.

To cancel a command through a dialog box, click **Cancel** or press Esc. To execute the command once you have filled out the dialog box, click **OK**. Click the **Help** button to get help with the dialog box. The on-line Help topic "Dialog Boxes" contains comprehensive information on using Minitab dialog boxes (see the section *Getting Help* on page 3-11).

Minitab Windows

When you are working with Minitab in Microsoft Windows or on a Macintosh, you have access to six types of Minitab windows, each of which offers a different perspective on your session. Minitab windows take full advantage of the operating environments; you can move, manipulate and resize them as you would any window. You can move among Minitab windows by clicking the window you want to activate or choosing the window you want from the **Window** menu. See your operating system documentation for more information as well as Minitab's on-line Help topic "Windows."

- **Data window.** The Data window displays the columns (variables) and rows (individual cases) of your data and makes it easy to enter and edit data into the worksheet.

The active cell is highlighted

Column number

Row number

Column name

To enter data into a cell, first click the cell to highlight it (it becomes the *active cell*), type the data value, then press Enter. You can also take full advantage of cut-and-paste operations to move individual cell values, columns or rows, selected blocks of data, or the entire worksheet. See the topic *Entering Data Using the Data Window* on page 4-2 and the on-line Help topic "Data Window" for comprehensive information on using the Data window most efficiently.

■ **Session window.** The Session window contains a record of all commands you have executed in the current session and their resulting non-graphical output. You can save the contents of the Session window to a text file, or you can work with the text in the Session window as you would in a word processor.

Choosing **Stat ➤ Basic Statistics ➤ Descriptive Statistics** is equivalent to typing the **DESCRIBE** Session command.

MTB> prompt; you can type session commands here or generate them using dialog boxes or the Command Line Editor.

Output from the Descriptive Statistics command

Whenever you issue a command from a menu, its corresponding session command appears in the Session window. You can type session commands directly into the Session window at the MTB> prompt, bypassing the menus. Minitab's **Edit ➤ Command Line Editor** command gives you further flexibility in that it lets you edit and re-execute commands executed earlier in your session. See the on-line Help topic "Session Window" for information on using all the Session window's features. The *Session Commands* section on page 3-8 gives more information on using session commands in the Session window.

■ **Graph window.** Whenever you create a high-resolution Minitab graph, it appears in its own Graph window. You can have one or many Graph windows open at the same time, and you can save an active Graph window to an image file using **File ➤ Save Window As**.

Graph title

Window title tells you graph type and variables plotted.

You can also create character-based graphs, which appear in the Session window. Chapter 6, *Graphs*, offers an overview of graphing in Minitab.

■ **Info window.** The Info window offers a quick overview of the current worksheet by summarizing its columns, stored constants, and matrices. It lists:
  – the names of all the columns that contain data, the number of present and missing values in each column
  – the names, values, and locations of all stored constants
  – matrices, along with their dimensions

An A displays next to each alpha column (a column that can contain non-numeric data). The Info window is updated automatically. DOS 8 has no Info window, instead use the INFO session command.

The Info window is particularly useful when you are working with a large worksheet and have difficulty remembering the names and locations of your variables. The session command INFO gives the same information as the Info window. You can make the Info window more useful by naming your columns.

- **History window.** The History window displays all the session commands and any data you entered from the Session window, without the output. This window provides a convenient overview of what you have done in your session. If you use the Data window to change the worksheet, a note is generated in the History window. The History window can contain approximately 64,000 characters of text. When this limit is reached, the first half of the contents is discarded without warning. If you need to be certain of capturing everything that appears in the History window, choose **File ➤ Other Files ➤ Start Recording History**. This beings recording your work in a journal file (equivalent to the session command JOURNAL). Choose **File ➤ Other Files ➤ Stop Recording History** (equivalent to the session command NOJOURNAL) to stop recording.

Commands used during your session

Note that you have changed the worksheet in the Data window.

You can use the History window to copy and paste commands into the Session window or the Command Line Editor, or as a basis for a *macro* (a file containing commands that execute a task). See the on-line Help topic "History Window" for more information (choose **Help ➤ Contents**, click **Windows**, then click **History Window**). DOS 8 has no History window, instead use JOURNAL and NOJOURNAL.

- **Help window.** The Help window offers indexed and cross-referenced access to the Minitab on-line Help system, a treasury of information on how to use Minitab. You can copy, paste, annotate, and print Help text using commands on the File and Edit menus when you are in Help. For more information on Help, see the *Getting Help* section on page 3-11.

The Minitab Worksheet

You usually begin a Minitab session by either retrieving a file containing data that have already been saved or entering a new data set. Minitab places the data that you either enter or retrieve into a temporary storage area called the *worksheet*. The worksheet, like any spreadsheet, is arranged into *columns* (variables) and *rows* (individual cases). A worksheet can also contain *stored constants* and *matrices*. If you want to use this worksheet later you should save it into a file (see *Saving Your Work* on page 4-14). If you don't save it before stopping Minitab, your current worksheet and its data disappear since they only existed in your computer's temporary memory.

Most of your work will be done with columns, which you can view in the Data window (depending on your version of Minitab). For example, the Pulse data set described in Chapter 1 appears in the Data window in columns as shown.

Columns. A column contains data for one variable, like pulse rate or sex. On most minicomputers and mainframe computers, you can use up to 1000 columns and constants and as many rows as your worksheet size will allow. Minitab automatically numbers columns in the worksheet as C1, C2, and so on. In Chapter 4 you will see how to assign names to your columns.

Rows. Each row contains one observation or case, numbered consecutively.

Stored Constants. On most minicomputers and mainframe computers, Minitab can store up to 1000 constants, each of which can contain a single number. You can refer to them by number (for example, K1, K2, K3, ..., K1000) or by name (for example, 'Temp' or 'IntRate'). To view a stored constant, choose **File ➤ Display Data** or choose **Window ➤ Info**. Stored constants do not appear in the Data window. Minitab automatically assigns the values of missing, e, and π to the last three stored constants: K998 = *; K999 = 2.71828; K1000 = 3.14159. You can change those values if you want.

Matrices. A worksheet accommodates up to 100 *matrices*, or rectangular blocks of cells, on most computers. You can refer to matrices by number (for example, M1, M2, ..., M100) or by name (for example, 'Inverse'). To view a stored matrix, choose **File ➤ Display Data**. Matrices do not appear in the Data window.

Session Commands

You can enter a command using the menus, if your version of Minitab and operating system allow it, or you can type the command after the MTB> prompt using the Minitab session command language. Most session commands are simple words that are easy to remember, like PLOT, TALLY, or PRINT, so they are easy to learn. If the MTB> prompt is the only thing you see when you start Minitab, you must use session commands. If the menu system is available to you, you may choose to use session commands for a variety of reasons, including the fact that once you learn them they are often quicker to use than menus. Choose **Window ➤ Session** to activate the Session window, and then enter your commands after the MTB> prompt.

Arguments. When you enter a session command, usually you enter one or more *arguments* after it. Arguments can be columns, constants, matrices, numbers, file names, or text strings. For example, "C1" is the argument in the following command, which tells Minitab to describe the data in column C1:

```
MTB > DESCRIBE C1
```

If you want to try this command, first retrieve the PULSE.MTW worksheet (see *Retrieving Data from a File* on page 4-17 for specific instructions). C1 contains resting pulse values. After typing the command DESCRIBE C1, press [Enter] to tell Minitab that the command is complete. (Press [Enter] after every command line.) Minitab displays the information you requested on the screen, and then prompts you for the next command with the MTB> prompt.

Command Syntax. When you use session commands, you must learn the words of an intuitive command language that communicate your instructions to Minitab. The set of rules by which the language operates is called the *command syntax*. A few commands allow fairly complicated expressions, but most use just a simple list of arguments. Appendix A lists all of Minitab's commands along with the correct syntax for including arguments. For example, the Describe command and its syntax look like this:

```
DESCRIBE the data in C...C
```

The C...C means you can type one or many columns after typing DESCRIBE. If you typed DESCRIBE C1 C2 C3, for example, Minitab would produce descriptive statistics for each column. You only need to type the items shown in bold type.

Subcommands. Many commands have subcommands that provide Minitab with more information. To signal Minitab that you want to use a subcommand, end the main command line with a semicolon (;) and then press [Enter]. Minitab then prompts you with the subcommand prompt, SUBC>. Type your subcommands, ending each line with a semicolon (;) and then press [Enter]. End the last subcommand with a period (.) to tell Minitab you are done with the command. Minitab then executes the entire command. When typing a command with no subcommand following, you do not have to type any punctuation mark after the command line.

This manual lists subcommand syntax immediately after the main command syntax, slightly indented. Here is an example of how the BY subcommand of DESCRIBE appears in a syntax box:

```
DESCRIBE the data in C...C
    BY C
```

For example, to describe the resting pulse data from PULSE.MTW (contained in C1) by gender (contained in C5), type the following, and be sure to include the punctuation marks indicated:

```
MTB > DESCRIBE C1;
SUBC>   BY C5.
```

If you forget to end the last subcommand with a period, you can type the period all by itself on the next SUBC> line. Minitab produces descriptive statistics for the resting pulses of each gender.

If you want to cancel a command that has a subcommand, type ABORT as the next subcommand.

When this manual introduces a new Minitab feature, it shows the menu path and dialog box associated with that feature, and then lists to the right the command syntax and a few of the most common subcommands. See Appendix A for a full list of commands and subcommands.

Syntax Conventions. Minitab uses the following conventions for worksheet and command elements.

C   denotes a column, such as C12.

K   denotes a constant, such as K14, which might represent, for example, the value 8.3.

E   denotes either a constant or a column, and sometimes a matrix.

M   denotes a matrix, such as M5.

[ ]   encloses an optional argument.

Observe the following conventions when entering session commands after the MTB> prompt:

1. You need only type the first four letters of a command or subcommand. Don't type the text that isn't bold in the syntax box.

2. Commands are not case-sensitive so you can type them in lowercase, uppercase, or a combination of both.

3. Start each command or subcommand on a new line and press Enter when you are done with each line.

4. You can continue a command or row of data onto the next line with the continuation symbol &.

5. Abbreviate lists of consecutive columns, stored constants, or matrices with a dash. For example, DESCRIBE C2-C5 is equivalent to DESCRIBE C2 C3 C4 C5.

6. Enclose file names and column names with single quotation marks (for example, DESCRIBE 'PULSE1').

In the PULSE.MTW worksheet, columns C1 through C4 are named PULSE1, PULSE2, RAN, and SMOKES. The commands that follow are all equivalent; they each produce descriptive statistics of those four columns. Column numbers and column names are interchangeable.

```
MTB > DESCRIBE C1 C2 'RAN' 'SMOKES'
MTB > DESCRIBE C1-C4
MTB > DESCRIBE c1-c4
MTB > DESC C1-C4
MTB > desc c1-c4
MTB > DESCRIBE 'PULSE1' 'PULSE2' 'RAN' 'SMOKES'
```

Getting Help

Minitab offers on-line Help at any point in a session. If you are using session commands, see page 2-8 for information that pertains to those releases. If you are using a version of Minitab that includes the menu system and on-line Help window, you have several ways to get help. You can choose any command in the Help menu, click the [Help] (or [?]) button in any dialog box, or press [F1] (DOS/Microsoft Windows) or [help] (Macintosh) to open the Help window, from which you can select a topic or search the index.

The rest of this section is specific to Release 9 and above for Macintosh and Windows. The structure of on-line Help for Release 8 is more like the structure described on page 2-8.

To open the Help table of contents, choose **Help ➤ Contents** (Microsoft Windows), or drag down on the Help menu [?] in the upper-right corner of your screen until your pointer is on Minitab Help, then release the mouse button (Macintosh).

The Minitab Contents window opens:

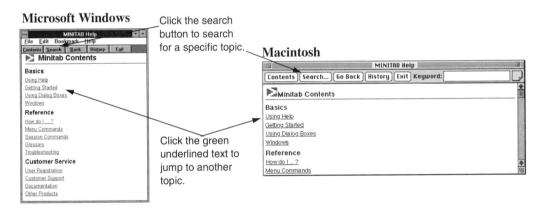

You can move from topic to topic by clicking underlined text. Throughout this book there are references to individual Help topics that give more information on a subject. To find a specific Help topic, click the Search button at the top of the screen to open the Search (or Index on the Macintosh) dialog box. (In Microsoft Windows, you can also go directly to the Search dialog box by choosing **Help ➤ Search for Help on.**)

To use the Search (or Index) dialog box:

Microsoft Windows: Type a word in the Search box that describes the keyword you are looking for. Notice as you begin typing, keywords show in the list box below which begin with the letters you are entering. When your keyword appears, click the Show Topics button. Double-click the topic you want to view.

Macintosh: Scroll through the Index window until you see the keyword you are looking for with its associated topics to the right. Double-click the topic you want to view.

Your Search dialog box should look like this:

1. Type your search word.

Microsoft Windows

1. Scroll through topics using the scroll bar until you find your topic.

2. Double-click the topic you want.

2. Click **Show Topics**.

Macintosh

3. Double-click the topic you want.

Minitab opens the Help window to the topic you selected. You can click Back (Microsoft Windows) or Go Back (Macintosh) to return to the previous topic. To return to the table of contents, click Contents. To open a list of all Help topics reviewed so far in your Help session, click History.

Alpha and Numeric Data

Minitab handles two types of data: numeric (numbers) and alpha (other characters). Graphics commands and data manipulation commands such as Sort and Copy can use alpha data; but most other analysis commands do not. Minitab displays the letter "A" beside column numbers in the Data and Info windows to indicate alpha columns.

When you want to use alpha data in a place where only numeric data are supported, choose **Manip ➤ Convert** to convert the alpha values into numeric values. For example, if you have a column containing the gender of a participant in an experiment that had the values Male and Female, you can convert all the values in the column to 1 and 2 respectively and store the results in another column.

Each alpha item (one row of a column) may be up to 80 characters. You may use any characters (letters, numbers, punctuation symbols, blanks). Columns cannot contain both alpha and numeric data: Minitab treats numbers appearing in an alpha column (as in a street address) as alpha characters. You can learn more about using alpha data by choosing **Help ➤ Contents**, clicking **Glossary**, and then clicking **alpha data**.

Symbols and Prompts

* **Missing Value Symbol.** Minitab uses an asterisk (*) in numeric columns and a blank in alpha columns to represent missing values. When you enter * as a value you do not have to enclose it in quotation marks unless the * is part of a command line (you will learn about entering data in the Chapter 4). Most commands exclude from analysis all rows with a missing value and display the number of excluded points. When an arithmetic command operates on a missing value, Minitab sets the result to *.

& Continuation Symbol. Type the continuation symbol & at the end of any Session window command line to indicate that the command or data row continues on to the next line. Minitab returns with the CONT> prompt.

 # Comment Symbol. Minitab ignores everything you type between the comment symbol # and the end of a Session window command line. You can use the symbol on any line. It is particularly useful when you are typing commands that you plan to save in a file and you want to explain some of the commands for the next user.

Minitab Prompts. Several different Session window prompts help you know what kind of input Minitab expects.

MTB>	Waiting for a command.
SUBC>	Waiting for a subcommand.
DATA>	Waiting for data. To finish entering data and return to the MTB> prompt, type END and press (Enter).
CONT>	Waiting for the rest of the command or data line continued from the previous line. If the previous line ends with the continuation symbol &, Minitab displays CONT> on the next line.
Continue?	Waiting for Y or (Enter) to continue displaying output, or N to discontinue displaying output. Your response to this prompt does not affect the execution of a command; it only affects the display of output on the screen. To suppress this prompt, type OH 0 (output height = 0). For example, OH 24 means that Minitab prints 24 lines on the screen at a time before prompting you with the Continue? prompt.

4
Managing Data

- **Entering data using the Data window**
  Cell Edit Mode
  Delete Cells, Delete Rows, and Erase Variables
  Inserting Cell and Inserting Rows
  Cut Cells and Paste/Insert Cells
  Undo
  Revert Worksheet and Restart Minitab
  Format Columns and Set Column Widths
  Compress Display

- **Entering data using session commands**
  READ
  SET
  INSERT
  RESTART
  NAME
  PRINT
  LET
  DELETE
  ERASE

- **Entering patterned data**
  Set Patterned Data (SET)

- **Saving your work**
  Save Window As
  Save Worksheet and Save Worksheet As (SAVE)
  WRITE
  Save Preferences
  Start/Stop Recording Session (OUTFILE/NOOUTFILE)

- **Retrieving data from a file**
  Open Worksheet (RETRIEVE)
  Import ASCII Data (READ)

- **Printing your work**
  Print Window

Data management involves entering, saving, retrieving, and printing data. In Minitab, you can enter data in whatever form is most convenient for you (depending on what your version of Minitab allows): typing it using the Data window or session commands, retrieving it from a file, pasting it or importing it from another application, or generating it. You can then save the worksheet in a variety of convenient file formats. Minitab also gives you options for storing the work you did in your session, including your analysis and its output. Finally, you can print all aspects of your work: the worksheet, graphs you used, the commands you used, and your statistical analysis.

Entering Data Using the Data Window

If your data are on paper and you need to type them into the Minitab worksheet, you can use either the Data window (if your version of Minitab supports it) or Minitab's data-entry session commands (see the next section).

The Data window information in this chapter is for Release 9 and 10 versions of Minitab. Release 8 has less extensive functionality, and different keyboard shortcuts. The *Changing Cell Values* and *Inserting Data* sections beginning on page 1-8 illustrate Release 8 functionality. The Session window information applies to all releases.

When you first start Minitab, the Data window appears at the bottom of the Minitab window. If the Data window doesn't appear, choose **Window ➤ Data**. You type your data, one value at a time, into the active cell (the one with the dark border), and then press ⌜Enter⌟. Pressing ⌜Enter⌟ accepts the entry and moves the active cell down or to the right, depending on the direction of the data entry arrow, so you can enter data either by column or by row.

Type column names here.

Click the maximize button to maximize the Data window.

Click the data entry arrow to change its direction. When it points down, pressing ⌜Enter⌟ moves the active cell down. When it points to the right, pressing ⌜Enter⌟ moves the active cell to the right.

The active cell; type the data value here.

Data Window Highlights

Enter data columnwise:

Click the arrow to
make it point down.

	C1-A	C2	C3
1	Owen		
2	Logan		
3	Baker		
4	■		
5			
6			

Click in row 1, column 1, then type:
  Owen (Enter)
  Logan (Enter)
  Baker (Enter)

Notice that after you type a value and press
(Enter), the active cell moves down.

Enter data rowwise:

Click the arrow to make it point to the right.

	C1-A	C2	C3
1	Owen	4	7 ■
2	Logan		
3	Baker		
4			
5			
6			

Click in row 1, column 2, then type:
  4 (Enter) 7 (Enter)

Notice that after you type a value and
press (Enter), the active cell moves right.

Enter data within a block:

	C1-A	C2	C3
1	Owen	4	7
2	Logan	5	8
3	Baker	6	9
4			
5			
6			

Highlight a block of cells:
- Point to the cell at row 2, column 2
- Press the left mouse button
- Drag to highlight the block
- Release the mouse button

Type:
  5 (Enter) 8 (Enter)
  6 (Enter) 9 (Enter)

Notice that if you highlight a block before typing values,
pressing (Enter) moves the active cell to the next cell in
the block.

Pressing any arrow key unhighlights the block.

"Big" carriage return:

Press Ctrl+Enter (Microsoft Windows) or ⌘+return (Macintosh) to move the active cell to beginning of the next column or row.

When the direction arrow points down, the active cell moves to the top of the next column.

When the direction arrow points right, the active cell moves to the beginning of the next row.

More tips:

To highlight an entire column, click the column number at the top of the column.

To highlight an entire row, click the row number.

To change the width of a column, point to the top of a line dividing two columns until the cursor becomes a two-sided arrow. Press the mouse button and drag the line.

To correct a value:

Click the cell, type the correct value, and press Enter

or

 – Double-click the cell
 – Delete old values and type new ones.

To undo a change:

If you have just typed a new value in a cell, and have not yet pressed Enter, press Esc to restore the previous value of the cell.

If you have just cut or pasted some data, choose **Edit ➤ Undo** to undo that cut or paste.

Active Cell Operations

The tasks in this section specify operations for active cells. Active cells have a dark rectangle around them.

To...	Do this
open the Data window	Choose **Window ➤ Data**, or Press [Ctrl]+[D] (Microsoft Windows) or [⌘]+[D] (Macintosh)
make an inactive cell active	Click the cell or move the arrow keys, [Tab], or [Enter] to reach the cell you want.
enter a new value into the active cell	Type the value, then press [Tab], [Enter], or an arrow key, or click another cell. The new value replaces the previous contents of the cell.
edit the contents of an existing cell	1. Enter cell edit mode: – double-click the cell, or – choose **Editor ➤ Cell Edit Mode**, or – press [Alt]+[Enter] (Microsoft Windows) or [option]+[return] (Macintosh) 2. Delete old text and type new text, using [Del] and/or [Backspace] to delete old text.. 3. To move within the cell, press – [Alt] + an arrow key (Microsoft Windows) – [option] + an arrow key (Macintosh) 4. Press [Enter] or click on another cell to exit edit mode and accept the changes.
enter or edit a column name Column name cell →	Click a column name cell, enter or edit a value as described above for data, then press [Enter]. Names can be up to 8 characters long. They cannot begin or end with a blank, include the symbol ' or #, or consist entirely of the symbol *.
clear the active cell	Press [Backspace] (Microsoft Windows) or [delete] (Macintosh), then press [Enter]. In a numeric column, Minitab inserts * in a cleared cell.
delete the active cell (and move other rows in the column up)	Choose **Edit ➤ Delete Cells**, or Press [Del] (Microsoft Windows) or [del⌦] (Macintosh).

To...	Do this
delete a row (and move the next row up)	Highlight the row by clicking the row number, then choose **Edit ➤ Delete Cells** or Choose **Manip ➤ Delete Rows** and complete the dialog box.
erase a column (this does not move other columns)	Highlight the column by clicking the column number, then choose **Edit ➤ Delete Cells** or press Del (Microsoft Windows) or del⌫ (Macintosh). Or, Choose **Manip ➤ Erase Variables** and complete the dialog box.
insert a cell above the active cell	Choose **Editor ➤ Insert Cell**.
insert a row above the active cell	Choose **Editor ➤ Insert Row**.
insert an empty column or columns between two existing column	Use cut and paste to move columns over as follows: 1. Highlight the column(s) to the right of where you want to insert the new column. 2. Cut the selected cells to the Clipboard by choosing **Edit ➤ Cut Cells**. 3. Click in the column name cell of the column after the blank columns that you want. 4. Choose **Edit ➤ Paste/Insert Cells** to bring the cells from the Clipboard back into the worksheet.
restore the previous value of the current cell before moving to another cell	Press Esc, or Choose **Edit ➤ Undo Change Within Cell**.
restore the worksheet to its last saved state and discard changes made since then	Choose **File ➤ Revert Worksheet**.

Changing Column Display

You can change the display of columns in the worksheet in the following ways:

To...	Do this
change the width of a single column	Point to the top of a line dividing two columns until you see a two-sided arrow ←|→ . Drag the border until the column is the desired width. Or, Choose **Editor ➤ Format Column**.
change the width of all columns	Choose **Editor ➤ Set Column Widths**.

To...	Do this
display a column with a fixed number of decimal places, or in exponential notation	Choose **Editor ➤ Format Column**.
hide or display empty, unnamed columns	Choose **Editor ➤ Compress Display**.
choose between automatic widening or fixed width for columns	Choose **Editor ➤ Format Column**, click either **Automatic Widening** or **Fixed Width**, and click **OK**.

Moving Around the Data Window

To move the active cell to...	Do this
any cell location	Choose **Editor ➤ Go To**.
one cell up, down, left, or right	Press an arrow key.
one cell right	Press `Tab`.
one cell right or down	Press `Enter` to move the active cell right or down, depending on the direction of the data entry arrow.
one screen down, up, left, or right or to the edge of the Data window	Press `Ctrl`+ an arrow key (Microsoft Windows) or `⌘`+ an arrow key (Macintosh). **Note**: `Page Up` and `Page Down` scroll the screen up and down, but *do not* move the active cell.
the beginning of the worksheet	Press `Ctrl`+`Home` (Microsoft Windows) or `⌘`+`home` (Macintosh).
the last used worksheet cell	Press `Ctrl`+`End` (Microsoft Windows) or `⌘`+`end` (Macintosh).
the beginning of the next row or column (depending on direction of the data entry arrow)	Choose **Editor ➤ Next Row/Column**, or Press `Ctrl`+`Enter` (Microsoft Windows) or `⌘`+`return` (Macintosh).
change the direction of the data entry arrow (this changes the behavior of the `Enter` and `Ctrl`+`Enter` (Microsoft Windows) or `⌘`+`return` (Macintosh) keys)	Click the data entry arrow, or Choose **Editor ➤ Change Entry Direction**.
return to the active cell when it is located off the display	Choose **Editor ➤ Go To Active Cell**.

Selecting Areas of the Worksheet

The active cell is always selected or part of a selected area. You can select areas of the worksheet for Cut and Paste operations or to form a limited entry area as follows:

To...	Do this
select any rectangular area	Drag from the first cell to the last cell.
select an entire row	Click the row number.
select an entire column	Click the column number.
adjust a selected area	Press [Shift] + an arrow key, or Press [Shift] and click on the cell to where you want to extend the area.

Cut, Copy, and Paste Features

You can perform the following Cut and Paste operations:

To...	Do this
copy the selected area of the worksheet to the Clipboard	Choose **Edit ➤ Copy Cells**.
replace a selected area of cells by pasting cells from the Clipboard into the worksheet	Choose **Edit ➤ Paste/Replace Cells**.
insert cells from the Clipboard. Existing cells that follow the active cell move down in the worksheet.	Choose **Edit ➤ Paste/Insert Cells**.
delete the selected area from the worksheet and put it on the Clipboard. Existing rows under the selected area move up to the selected area.	Choose **Edit ➤ Cut Cells**.
delete the selected area from the worksheet without putting it on the Clipboard. Existing rows under the selected area move up to the selected area.	Choose **Edit ➤ Delete Cells**, or Press [Del] (Microsoft Windows) or [del⇦] (Macintosh).
undo your last cut or paste operation	Choose **Edit ➤ Undo Cut/Paste**.

Entering Data Using Session Commands

If your version of Minitab allows it, you might find that you prefer entering data using the Data window, in which case you can skip this section. There are three session commands for entering data into the current worksheet by typing it on the keyboard: READ, SET, and INSERT. The READ command lets you type data into the worksheet row by row. The SET command lets you type data into the worksheet one column at a time. You can also use SET to enter patterned data (data with repeating or incremental values). The INSERT command lets you insert new rows of data between established rows or add data at the beginning or end of a column.

If you want to clear the current worksheet of any data that you don't care to save before you enter new data, use the RESTART command, which clears the worksheet without your having to leave Minitab; just type RESTART after the prompt.

A few conventions apply to entering data from the keyboard:

1. Minitab reads numbers with decimal points or in exponential notation (for example, 123.4 or 1.234E2).

2. Separate column entries by pressing [Spacebar] or using commas. Do not include commas within a column entry (for example, type 6492, not 6,492).

3. The missing value code (∗) is a valid data point.

4. You can continue data lines by typing & at the end of the line. This tells Minitab to read all values on the following line as part of the same row.

5. Type END after the last data line.

The examples in this section use the year and cost data shown below; you can work through this section by entering the commands as they are shown after the MTB> prompt and then after the DATA> prompt.

Naming Columns Using NAME

It is a good idea to name columns you intend to keep right away so that you won't forget what they contain.

```
NAME C 'name' ... C 'name'
```

To name the first two columns of the worksheet, where C1 contains the year and C2 contains the cost, type:

```
MTB > NAME C1 'Year'   C2 'Cost'
```

When instructing Minitab to operate on a column, you can refer to it by number or name. Column names are not case-sensitive, so you can use lowercase or uppercase names (for example, you can call a column 'YEAR' or 'year' or 'Year'; it won't matter to Minitab). Names can be up to 8 characters long, with no leading or trailing spaces, no single quotation marks ('), and no octothorpes (#). A name cannot consist of a single asterisk (∗). The session commands in most versions of Minitab require that you enclose names in single quotation marks when you enter them as arguments.

Entering Data by Row Using READ

When you need to type new data in from the keyboard one row at a time, use the READ command. If there are any data in the columns you list, READ erases those data and replaces them with the new data you enter.

```
READ C...C
```

For example, say you need to enter the following data set into the first two columns of the current Minitab worksheet.

To tell Minitab that you want these data in the first two columns, type the following command after the MTB> prompt:

```
MTB > READ C1 C2
```

Minitab responds with the DATA> prompt. Type the data in, row by row, inserting at least one blank space between each data value. Press ⌐Enter⌐ after each row to tell Minitab you are ready to begin the next row.

```
DATA> 1992 1.50
DATA> 1993 1.52
DATA> 1994 1.55
DATA> 1995 1.75
DATA> 1996 1.80
```

When you are finished, type END:

```
DATA> END
```

C1 and C2 now contain the data you typed. Note that to enter alpha data with READ, you must use the FORMAT subcommand. See on-line Help for more information.

Viewing Data Using PRINT

The PRINT command prints the data you request on your screen. You can command Minitab to print any combination of columns, stored constants, or matrices.

```
PRINT E...E
```

For example, to have Minitab display the columns from the previous example on the screen, type:

```
MTB > PRINT C1 C2
```

Minitab displays the data as shown:

```
ROW   Year   Cost

  1   1992   1.50
  2   1993   1.52
  3   1994   1.55
  4   1995   1.75
  5   1996   1.80
```

Entering Data One Column at a Time Using SET

The SET command works just like the READ command except that the data are entered by column and not by row.

```
SET C
```

It may be quicker to enter the year and cost data by column rather than by row using SET:

```
MTB > SET C1
DATA>   1992 1993 1994 1995 1996
DATA> END
MTB > SET C2
DATA>   1.50 1.52 1.55 1.75 1.80
DATA> END
MTB > PRINT C1 C2

 ROW   Year   Cost

   1    1992   1.50
   2    1993   1.52
   3    1994   1.55
   4    1995   1.75
   5    1996   1.80
```

When data are already in a column you specify with SET, SET erases those data and uses the new data you enter.

Correcting Errors

If you make a mistake entering data and need to change a number, use the LET command.

```
LET C(K) = K
```

While the LET command has many uses (see Chapter 5), in this context it replaces a single value in a specified column and row with a new value. For example, to change the value in C2 row 3 (currently 1.50 if you have been following the examples) to 1.68, type:

```
MTB > LET C2(3) = 1.68
```

To change an entire row or rows, use the DELETE command to delete the row and the INSERT command to replace it with a new row (since the DELETE command moves up the remaining rows to close the gap).

```
DELETE rows K...K of C...C
```

For example, type the following command to delete row 4 from columns C1 and C2:

```
MTB > DELETE 4 C1-C2
```

You can use the PRINT command (PRINT C1-C2) to see how the worksheet changes.

You can abbreviate a list of consecutive rows by using a colon (:). To delete rows 1 through 3 from C1, type:

```
MTB > DELETE 1:3 C1
```

If you need to erase columns, constants, or matrices, use the ERASE command.

ERASE E...E

For example, to erase C1 altogether, type:

```
MTB > ERASE C1
```

The E in the syntax statement means you can type C for column, K for constant, or M for matrix. It is a good practice to erase all data you no longer need; it's easier to keep track of what you are doing.

Adding Data to Existing Columns Using INSERT

The INSERT command inserts rows of data into the worksheet at the location you specify: at the top, between two rows, or at the bottom.

INSERT [between rows K K] C...C

For example, if you had entered the year and cost data introduced earlier in this chapter, you could insert two new rows at the top of columns C1-C2 (if you want to follow this example you'll need to first re-enter the data shown earlier using READ or SET and then try the INSERT command):

```
MTB > INSERT 0 1 C1-C2
DATA>    1990 1.44
DATA>    1991 1.45
DATA> END
```

Note that the INSERT command requires that the specified columns already contain data. Minitab reads the space between 0 and 1 as the top of the column. To insert data between rows 5 and 6 of columns C1-C2, type:

```
MTB > INSERT 5 6 C1-C2
DATA>    1994 1.58
DATA> END
```

Finally, to place data at the bottom of columns C1-C2, type:

```
MTB > INSERT C1-C2
```

If you insert data into just one column, you can string the data across the data lines as with SET. You can also use patterned data abbreviations (described in the next section).

Entering Patterned Data

When you need to place patterned data (data with repetitive or incremental values) into a column, **Calc ➤ Set Patterned Data** (equivalent to the SET session command) can save you a lot of typing.

For example, to set C3 with the numbers 1, 2, 3, 4, and 5:

Dialog box	**Session command**
Choose **Calc ➤ Set Patterned Data**.	``` MTB > SET C3
Type C3 in **Store result in column** and then press Tab.	DATA> 1:5
	DATA> END
Type 1 in **Start at**, press Tab, type 5 in **End at**, and then click **OK**.	MTB > PRINT C3

```
MTB > SET C3
DATA>    1:5
DATA> END
MTB > PRINT C3

C3
   1    2    3    4    5
```

Notice that you use a colon to abbreviate the range using the SET session command. A slash indicates an increment. Put lists that you want repeated into parentheses. There must be no space between the repeat factor and the corresponding parenthesis. If the repeat factor is before the parentheses, Minitab repeats the entire list; if it is after, Minitab repeats each number in the range. You cannot nest parentheses. You can use a stored constant in place of any number on a data line after SET. This list illustrates other conventions for setting columns with patterns when using SET:

4:1	expands to 4, 3, 2, 1
1:3/.5	expands to 1, 1.5, 2, 2.5, 3
3(1)	expands to 1, 1, 1
3(1:3)	expands to 1, 2, 3, 1, 2, 3, 1, 2, 3
(1:3)2	expands to 1, 1, 2, 2, 3, 3
3(1:3)2	expands to 1, 1, 2, 2, 3, 3, 1, 1, 2, 2, 3, 3, 1, 1, 2, 2, 3, 3

Saving Your Work

Whenever you are dealing with data that you plan to use in the future, you should periodically save it in a more permanent form so that your labor is not lost. You have a number of options for saving, depending on the nature of your work and what you need saved (be it the data, the command sequence from a given session, Minitab output, graphics, and so on). To save the contents of any window, choose **File ➤ Save Window As** while the window you want to save is active. If you are using Minitab for Microsoft Windows or the Macintosh, consult the appropriate operating system documentation for information on using the Save dialog boxes to choose locations for your files.

Saving the Worksheet as a Minitab File

The current worksheet consists of the data Minitab has in its memory. If you've just entered data into the worksheet, it resides in the temporary memory of your computer. To save an exact copy of the current worksheet, including cell contents, column names, constants, and matrices, use either **File ➤ Save Worksheet** (if this is the first time you've saved the worksheet or you want to overwrite the old version of the current worksheet with the new version) or **File ➤ Save Worksheet As** (if you want to save the worksheet with a new file name), both equivalent to the SAVE session command.

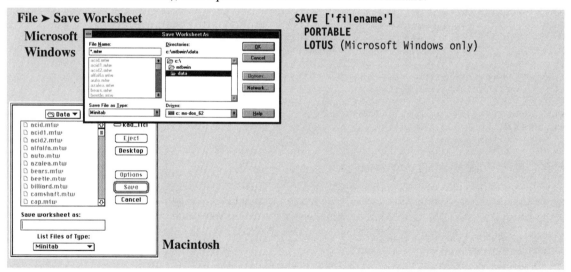

For example, to save a worksheet containing data on a market analysis study:

Dialog box	Session command
Choose **File ➤ Save Worksheet**.	SAVE 'MARKET'
Type Market in **File Name**, select the directory you want, and then click **OK**.	

Minitab creates a file with the extension MTW, signifying that the file is a saved Minitab worksheet. An MTW file is a highly efficient way to store data, because Minitab can retrieve MTW files very quickly. Choose any file name you want (excluding leading blanks and the symbols # and '). If you omit a file name, Minitab saves the worksheet in a file named MINITAB.MTW. If you are using session commands and you want to save your worksheet on a disk or in a directory other than your current working area, include the full path name within single quotation marks. (See your System Administrator if you are unable to save a file without path information.)

Saving Worksheet Data in Other Formats

MTW files created with **File ➤ Save Worksheet As** are designed to be used only by Minitab. If you want to be able to open a Minitab worksheet on a different kind of computer or a different program, you can save the file in a different file type. You can also use the Copy, Cut and Paste commands on the Edit menu to copy or cut data to the Clipboard and then paste it into other applications that support cutting and pasting. See on-line Help for more information.

Using File ➤ Save Worksheet As. If you are running Minitab for Microsoft Windows or the Macintosh, you can save a Minitab worksheet in any of the file types that appear in the **Save File as Type** (**List Files of Type** on the Macintosh) drop-down list.

1. Choose **File ➤ Save Worksheet As**.

2. Click (or drag down on the Macintosh) the list arrow to open the list of file types.

3. Click the file type (or, on the Macintosh, release the mouse button on the file type).

Portable Minitab file that you can open in Minitab on any operating system

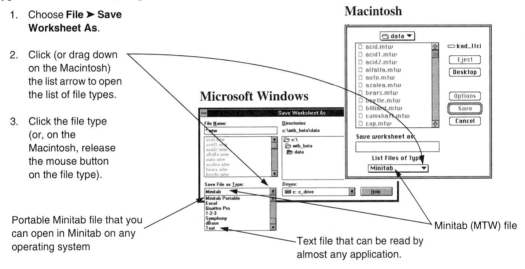

Text file that can be read by almost any application.

Minitab (MTW) file

Using Session Commands. If you are using an older version of Minitab or using session commands, you use the SAVE session command to save the worksheet as a Minitab worksheet. Use the PORTABLE subcommand with SAVE to save the worksheet as a portable Minitab file that you can open in Minitab on any operating system. For DOS and Microsoft Windows, the LOTUS subcommand saves to a file in Lotus 1-2-3 format

You can save the columns in your current worksheet to an ASCII text file, also called a *data file*, using the WRITE command. Minitab automatically assigns data files the extension DAT. DAT files contain columns of data as ASCII text; they do not include stored constants or column names.

```
WRITE ['filename'] C...C
```

If you omit a file name, Minitab writes the columns to your screen, close together, with no column names or row numbers. If you are writing to a file, Minitab adjusts the format to make the data as compact as possible. The number of columns that can be put on one line varies with the data. If all columns do not fit on one line, Minitab puts the continuation symbol & at the end of the line and continues the data onto the next line. When writing columns of unequal length to a file, Minitab makes them equal by adding missing value symbols (*) to the shorter columns. You can use the FORMAT subcommand to specify the number of characters for a given column, which can help make your output easier to read. See on-line Help for more information.

Saving Your Minitab Session

In a given session you will often apply a wide range of analysis to your data, reading Minitab's output on the screen as you go along. If you are using Minitab for Microsoft Windows or the Macintosh, you can save the contents of the Session window using the **File ➤ Save Window As** command. Since the Session window can hold up to about 15,000 lines at one time, your entire session might not be saved, so you might want to use an outfile if your session is a long one, or you can use the **File ➤ Save Preferences ➤ Session Window** command to automatically save your session in a backup file. See on-line Help for more information.

Minitab Outfiles. Use **File ➤ Other Files ➤ Start Recording Session** (equivalent to the OUTFILE session command) to send all subsequent commands and output to a permanent text file (with the extension LIS, for listing) that you can refer to when you need to remember what you did during a given session.

File ➤ Other Files ➤ Start Recording Session

```
OUTFILE ['filename']
NOOUTFILE
```

Start Recording Session

◉ Record output in file and display in Session window
○ Record output in file only

☐ Set output width to: [   ]
☐ Set output height to: [   ]

[Help]   [Select File]   [Cancel]

Once you start recording the session, Minitab sends a copy of everything that appears on the screen (except high-resolution graphics) to the specified file. When the session is over, end the outfile by choosing **File ➤ Other Files ➤ Stop Recording Session** (or using the NOOUTFILE session command).

If you specify a file name that already contains previous session work, Minitab adds the new output onto the end of the original LIS file.

Retrieving Data from a File

Earlier in this chapter you saw how to enter data into the Minitab worksheet by typing it or generating it. You can also retrieve it from a saved file in any of a variety of file formats.

Opening a Minitab Worksheet

Use **File ➤ Open Worksheet** (equivalent to the RETRIEVE session command) to open a saved file.

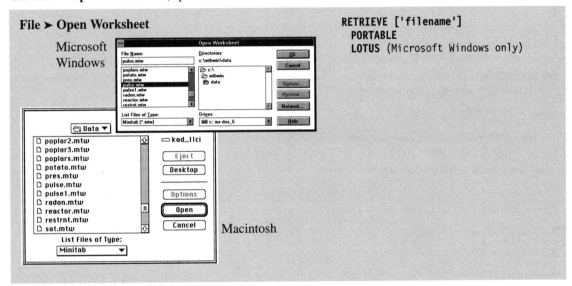

Minitab includes a number of sample data sets from various sources that are installed along with Minitab. The exact location of these files depends on your version of Minitab and the computer you are using. Check with your System Administrator if you are not sure where the sample data sets are stored on your system. For example, if you wanted to open the PULSE.MTW file, use the following commands:

Dialog box	Session command
Choose **File ➤ Open Worksheet**.	**Microsoft Windows:** MTB > RETRIEVE 'C:\MTBWIN\DATA\PULSE.MTW'
Select the directory containing the file.	**Macintosh:** MTB > RETRIEVE 'MYDISK:Minitab 10.5:Data:PULSE.MTW'
Scroll the **File Name** list to find the file, double-click the file, and then click **OK**.	**Vax/VMS:** MTB > RETRIEVE 'MTB_DIR:PULSE'
	Unix (Sun/SunOS): MTB > RETRIEVE '/usr/local/minitab/sav/pulse'

This places the PULSE data in the current Minitab worksheet, ready for you to analyze. Retrieving a saved worksheet always erases any data from the existing worksheet before replacing it with the new worksheet.

Opening Files in Other Formats

If the file you want to open has one of the file types mentioned in the previous section, you can use the Open Worksheet dialog box and select the file type from the **List Files of Type** drop-down list. If the file type is not mentioned, then save the data in the other application in a text file and then open it in Minitab. You can also use the Copy, Cut and Paste commands on the Edit menu to copy or cut data to the Clipboard within a different application that supports cutting and pasting and then paste it into Minitab. See Help for more information.

If you are using session commands, you can use RETRIEVE with the PORTABLE and LOTUS subcommands as mentioned in the previous section. To retrieve data files in ASCII format created by other packages you can use READ, SET, or INSERT. The READ command, for example, enters data saved as ASCII characters one row at a time into one or more worksheet columns. If the file contains just rows and columns of numbers, with at least one space or a comma between columns, and where each row of data is no more than 160 spaces long, then you can use READ without a subcommand. For example, to import the file MYDATA.DAT into columns C1-C10, type:

```
MTB > READ 'MYDATA' C1-C10
```

If the file contains alpha characters, if there are no spaces between columns of data, or if there are blanks for missing values, you will then need to use the READ subcommand called FORMAT to import the file. For help on using FORMAT, use on-line Help for information.

Printing

If you are using Minitab for Microsoft Windows or the Macintosh, you can print the contents of any window that is active by choosing **File ➤ Print Window**. In this way you can print the worksheet with the Data window active, your session with the Session window active, a graph with the Graph window active, your command list with the History window active, and so on. You will be given different printing options depending on the window and whether or not you highlighted a section of the window.

If you are using session commands or an older version of Minitab, the easiest way to obtain hard copies of your session work and worksheet contents is by creating an outfile (described earlier in this chapter). Once you have started an outfile, use Minitab's PRINT command to display worksheet data on the screen, and, simultaneously, to send it to your outfile. When your session is over, you can open the outfile in a text editor or word processor, edit it as necessary, and then print it from there. Because the OUTFILE command saves everything in the session, the LIS file may contain much more than you actually want, so editing it before printing it is not a bad idea. You can also use OUTFILE to save only certain portions of a Minitab session.

To print worksheet data in a more compact form, you can use the WRITE command discussed earlier in this chapter. WRITE sends the data to a data file in a compact format but does not show column names. Print this data file by opening it in a text editor or word processor and printing it from there. Use this method when you want to print a large volume of output efficiently.

Minitab File Summary

MTW	Minitab worksheet. A binary file that stores worksheet data — rows and columns of data, variable names, and Data window settings. Can be used only by Minitab on the same computer operating system (such as Microsoft Windows) that saved it. To open a worksheet, choose **File ➤ Open Worksheet** or **File ➤ Merge Worksheet**. To save an MTW file, choose **File ➤ Save Worksheet As**. You cannot print or edit a Minitab worksheet outside of Minitab.
MTP	Portable worksheet. Used to transfer data saved by Minitab on one operating system, such as a Macintosh, to another, such as Microsoft Windows. Contains data columns, constants, and matrices in ASCII format. To open a portable worksheet, choose **File ➤ Open Worksheet** or **File ➤ Merge Worksheet**. To save the current worksheet as a portable worksheet, choose **File ➤ Save Worksheet As**.
DAT, TXT	Text file. Also called ASCII. Most applications, including Minitab, can open and save text files. You can also print and/or edit a text file outside of Minitab. To open a text file, choose **File ➤ Open Worksheet**, **File ➤ Merge Worksheet**, or **File ➤ Other Files ➤ Import ASCII Data**. To save the current worksheet as a text file, choose **File ➤ Save Worksheet As** or **File ➤ Other Files ➤ Export ASCII Data.**
MGF	Minitab Graphics Format file (Release 9 Enhanced and above). MGF files can be saved and opened only by Minitab. Once an MGF file is open, however, you can copy it to the Clipboard or print it to the printer. To view an MGF file, choose **File ➤ Open Graph**. To save the active Graph window in an MGF file, choose **File ➤ Save Window As**.
TXT, LIS	Saved session file. A text (ASCII) file which stores some or all of the Session window. You can edit and/or print saved session files outside of Minitab. To save your session in a saved session file, choose **Edit ➤ Save Preferences ➤ Session Window** and select the desired options, and/or choose **File ➤ Save Window As**, and/or choose **File ➤ Other Files ➤ Start Recording Session**.
TXT, MTJ	History file. A text (ASCII) file which stores the session commands used during a Minitab session. You can use this file to assemble a macro or to re-execute previously executed commands. To save commands in a history file, while the History window is active, choose **File ➤ Save Window As**. Or, when you are ready to begin saving commands, choose **File ➤ Other Files ➤ Start Recording History**.
MAC	%Macro file (Release 9 and above). A text (ASCII) file that contains commands you can execute as a local or global macro. To invoke, type %filename, where filename is the name of the file with a MAC extension.
MTB	Exec file. A text (ASCII) file that contains commands you can execute as a macro called an Exec. To invoke, choose **File ➤ Other Files ➤ Run an Exec**.
STARTUP.MAC STARTUP.MTB	Special macro files that automatically execute when you start a new Minitab session.

5
Manipulating and Analyzing Data

- **Copy, group, sort, and code data**
  Copy, Paste, and Copy Columns (COPY)
  Sort (SORT)
  Code Data Values (CODE)

- **Perform arithmetic transformations**
  Mathematical Expressions (LET)
  Column Statistics
  Row Statistics

- **Obtain basic descriptive statistics on a variable**
  Descriptive Statistics (DESCRIBE)

- **Perform more detailed analyses, including t-confidence intervals, t-tests, correlation, regression, analysis of variance, categorization of data, and χ^2 analysis**
  1-Sample t (TINTERVAL and TTEST)
  2-Sample t (TWOT and TWOSAMPLE)
  Correlation (CORRELATION)
  Regression (REGRESS)
  Oneway (ONEWAY)
  Oneway (Unstacked) (AOVONEWAY)
  Cross Tabulation (TABLE)

Minitab can perform a wide variety of statistical analyses; this chapter illustrates a small sample of commonly-used Minitab procedures, beginning with commands that edit and manipulate data, and then moving to commands that give detailed statistical information. The sampling of commands in this chapter includes only selected subcommands. For a complete list of commands, subcommands, and command syntax, refer to Appendix A.

Every command described in this chapter is accompanied by an example showing its use and the output it produces. The examples use data that either appear right on the page or come with the sample data set directory accompanying every release of Minitab, so you can try the examples yourself on your computer. For information on entering data into Minitab and retrieving sample data sets, see Chapter 4.

Once you have mastered the examples in this chapter and are ready to learn new commands, turn to Appendix A. Choose one of the topics and then scan the list for the command name or menu command that you want to learn more about. Use Minitab's Help for information about the command and how to interpret its output (see *Getting Help* on page 3-11 for more information).

Editing and Manipulating Data

Minitab has many useful ways to edit and manipulate data, including **Copy Columns**, **Sort**, and **Code Data Values**. Other Manip menu commands you can explore on your own include **Rank** (to store the rank values of the data in a column), **Stack** and **Unstack** (to stack columns on top of each other into one long column or to unstack a long column into groups of columns), **Convert** (to convert alpha data to numbers or numbers to alpha data), and **Concatenate** (to merge rows of alpha data in a given set of columns into single longer rows).

Copying Data

Minitab offers two primary options for copying data from one block of cells to another. You can either copy in the Data window using **Edit ➤ Cut** and **Edit ➤ Paste**, or you can use **Manip ➤ Copy Columns** (equivalent to the COPY session command). **Copy Columns** gives you greater flexibility and lets you copy only a subset of data easily.

Copying in the Data Window. When you want to copy a limited amount of data, it can be quickest to use the Data Window and the **Edit ➤ Cut** and **Edit ➤ Paste** commands. In this example, you copy the data in C1, which you can enter if you want to follow the example, to the destination block starting with row 1, C4:

1. Highlight the cells containing the data, then choose **Edit ➤ Copy Cells**.

2. Click the first cell in the destination block, then choose **Edit ➤ Paste/Insert** Cells.

Using Copy Columns (COPY). For copying larger blocks or subsets of data, use **Manip ➤ Copy Columns** (**Manip ➤ Copy Columns** for Release 8), equivalent to the COPY session command.

Manip ➤ Copy Columns

```
COPY C...C into C...C
  USE rows K...K
  USE rows where C = K...K
  OMIT rows K...K
  OMIT rows where C = K...K
```

Manip ➤ Copy Columns copies all or a subset of data from columns, constants, and matrices to new columns, constants, and matrices. For example, to copy column C1 to C4, use the following commands (the example uses the data shown earlier):

Dialog box	Session command
Choose **Manip ➤ Copy Columns**.	`MTB > COPY C1 C4`
Type HT in **Copy from columns**, press (Tab), type C4 in **To columns**, and then click **OK**.	

Copying a Subset of Data. Manip ➤ Copy Columns copies an entire column or block of columns into the new location. You can copy a subset of the rows using **Use Rows** and **Omit Rows** in the Copy Columns dialog box (equivalent to the USE and OMIT Session subcommands). **Use Rows** tells which rows to copy and **Omit Rows** tells which rows not to copy. For example, say columns C1-C2 contain information on a set of people, and C3 contains their genders, coded by male = 0 and female = 1. To copy only the information on the males into a new column block (C12-C13), use the following commands (using the data entered earlier):

Dialog box	**Session command**

Choose **Manip ➤ Copy Columns**

```
MTB > COPY C1-C2 C12-C13;
SUBC>    USE C3 = 0.
```

Click **Use Rows**.

This changes the worksheet as follows:

C1	C2	C3		C12	C13
HT	WT	GENDER			
66	135	1		70	155
70	155	0	→	64	145
64	145	0		64	140
64	140	0		69	160
63	108	1			
69	160	0			

You can also specify a range of values in the **Use rows with column equal to** box (equivalent to the Session USE subcommand). For example, specifying **Use rows with column HT equal to 0:64** (equivalent to the Session subcommand USE 'HT' = 0:64) copies only the subjects between 0 and 64 inches tall, inclusive. To copy only certain rows, like the first, third, fourth, and fifth, simply enter the rows you want to use in the **Use rows** box, or type the Session subcommand USE 1 3:5. The **Omit Rows** option works the same way; entering 2 and 6 in the **Omit rows** box in the Omit Rows dialog box (equivalent to the Session subcommand OMIT 2 6) copies rows 1, 3, 4, and 5 to the new column block.

Sorting a Column

To arrange the numbers in a column in ascending or descending numerical (or alphabetical) order, use
Manip ➤ Sort (**Calc ➤ Sort** for Release 8),, equivalent to the SORT session command.

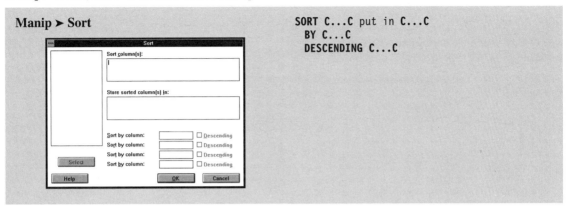

For example, if C1 Depth contains lake depths from eight lakes in a national park, you can order the data
from shallowest to deepest, placing the results in C3, using the following commands (enter the Depth and
Sector data shown below if you want to try the example):

Dialog box	Session command
Choose **Manip ➤ Sort**.	MTB > SORT C1 C3
Type Depth in **Sort column(s)**, press Tab, and then type C3 in **Store sorted column(s) in**.	
Click the first **Sort by column** box, type Depth, and then click **OK**.	

This sorts C1 and places the new list in ascending order in C3:

C1 Depth	C2 Sector		C3
245	3		130
208	3		177
287	1	→	208
130	2		221
255	1		240
240	1		245
177	3		255
221	1		287

Column C2 Sector (a marker for lake location) stays the same. If you want to carry along C2, then use the following commands:

Dialog box	Session command
Choose **Manip ➤ Sort**.	MTB > SORT C1 C2 C3 C4
Type Depth Sector in **Sort column(s)**, press Tab, and then type C3 C4 in **Store sorted column(s) in**.	
Type Depth in the first **Sort by column** box, and then click **OK**.	

This time Minitab sorts C1 and places it into C3, carrying along the values from C2 and placing them in C4, as shown below:

C1	C2		C3	C4
Depth	Sector			
245	3		130	2
208	3		177	3
287	1	→	208	3
130	2		221	1
255	1		240	1
240	1		245	3
177	3		255	1
221	1		287	1

Sorting by a Different Column (BY). In a standard sort, Minitab sorts based on the column you enter in the **Sort by column** box, or, if you are using session commands, on the first column you specify; in this example, C1. To have Minitab sort based on a different column (or different columns), specify that column in the **Sort by column** box (equivalent to the BY Session subcommand) as in the following example.

Dialog box	Session command
Manip ➤ Sort	MTB > SORT C2 C3 C4 C12 C13 C14; SUBC> BY C3 C4.

In this set of commands, Minitab sorts C2, C3, and C4 first by C3 and, when there is a tie between any values in C3, uses C4 as the next sorting criteria. Minitab carries along the values in C2 and C4, placing the whole block in C12, C13, and C14. When there are unresolved ties, Minitab sorts the data according to their original placement.

Sorting in Descending Order (DESCENDING). You can sort columns in descending order by clicking the **Descending** box next to the **Sort by column** box (equivalent to the DESCENDING subcommand). For example, to sort the first column of a three-column worksheet in descending order, carrying along C2 and C3 (you can follow the example by restarting Minitab and entering the data shown):

Dialog box	Session command
| Choose **Manip ➤ Sort**. | ```
MTB > SORT C1 C2 C3   C1 C2 C3;
SUBC>   DESCENDING C1.
``` |
Type **C1 C2 C3** in **Sort Column(s)**, press [Tab], type **C1 C2 C3** in **Store sorted column(s) in**.	
Type **C1** in **Sort by column**, then click **Descending**.	
Click **OK**.	

This changes the worksheet as follows:

```
C1  C2  C3          C1  C2  C3
 2  10  -1           5  14  -3
 3  11  -1           4  13  -1
 1  12  -3     →     3  11  -1
 4  13  -1           2  10  -1
 5  14  -3           1  12  -3
```

You can also sort to different columns if you want to preserve the original data. If you are using the SORT session command rather than the dialog box, note that columns listed after DESCENDING must also be listed after BY or must be the first column listed after SORT if no BY is used. Minitab sorts alpha data in alphabetical order.

Coding a Column into Categories

Manip ➤ Code Data Values (**Calc➤ Code Data Values** in Release 8) , equivalent to the CODE session command, recodes one or more columns, searching the specified column for a value or set of values and replacing them with a new value. Tell Minitab the value or range of values that you want a given code to cover, and it produces a new column assigning a code to each observation.

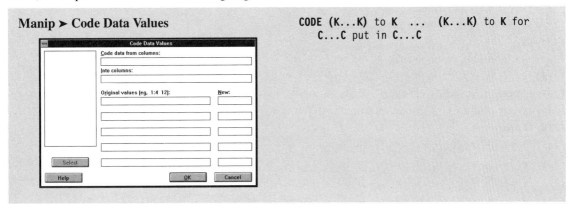
```

For example, suppose C1 contains the heights of 10 trees. To classify trees of 76 inches or less as short (using a code of 1), and trees of more t.han 76 inches as tall (using a code of 2), and place the classifications in C2, use the following commands (you can perform the example by restarting Minitab and entering the data shown following the exhibit in C1):

Dialog box	Session command
Choose **Manip ➤ Code Data Values**.	MTB > CODE (0:76)1 (77:999)2 C1 C2

Type C1 in **Code data from columns**, press Tab, type C2 in **Into columns**, and press Tab.

Type 0:76 in the first **Original values** text box, press Tab, type 1 in **New**, and press Tab.

Type 77:999 in the second **Original values** text box, press Tab, type 2 in **New**, and then click **OK**.

The worksheet now looks like this:

C1	C2
70	1
65	1
63	1
72	1
81	2
83	2
66	1
75	1
80	2
75	1

You can also use **Code Data Values** to change values into *, the missing data code. For example, to change −99 to * use the following commands:

Dialog box	Session command
Choose **Manip ➤ Code Data Values**.	MTB > CODE (-99) '*' C1-C5 C1-C5

Type C1-C5 in **Code data from columns**, press Tab, type C1-C5 in **Into columns**, and press Tab.

Type -99 in the first **Original values** text box, press Tab, type * in **New**, and then click OK.

You can place up to 50 original values or ranges into the five **Original values** boxes in the Code Data Values dialog box or after the CODE session command. You can specify up to 30 columns in one command (15 input, 15 output).

Transforming Data

To create a new column of data that is a function of an existing column, you use **Calc ➤ Mathematical Expressions** or **Calc ➤ Functions**, equivalent to the LET session command. These commands perform many different operations on values you specify. You create expressions that are made up of arithmetic, comparison, or logical operators or a variety of row and column functions, including logarithms, standard deviations, and square roots. Appendix A contains a complete list. Arguments may be columns, stored constants, or numbers, but not matrices.

Arithmetic, Comparison, and Logical Operations

Minitab uses the following symbols for the operators you can enter into an expression (Appendix A contains a complete list, including trigonometric and other functions):

**	raise to a power
*	multiplication
/	division
+	addition
-	subtraction
= or EQ	equal to
~= or NE	not equal to
< or LT	less than
> or GT	greater than
<= or LE	less than or equal to
>= or GE	greater than or equal to
& or AND	logical "and"
| or OR	logical "or"
~ or NOT	logical "not"

Minitab performs all these operations on rows; for example, the following commands add the value in each row of C1 to that in each row of C2 and place the resulting sum in the corresponding row of C10.

Dialog box	**Session command**
Choose **Calc ➤ Mathematical Expressions**.	`MTB > LET C10 = C1 + C2`

Type C10 in **Variable (new or modified)**, press Tab twice, type C1 + C2 in **Expression**, and then click **OK**.

The worksheet now contains a new column, as shown here:

C1	C2	C10
5	2	7
15	1	16

If any element of a row is missing, Minitab sets the result to *, the missing value symbol. If an operation is impossible, like dividing by 0, Minitab sets that result to missing and prints a "value out of bounds" message. **Mathematical Expressions** sets true comparisons to 1 and false ones to 0. You can use the logical comparison operators to group your data.

For example, suppose C1 contains the heights of trees and C2 contains a code indicating species (1 = hickory, 2 = white oak). To copy into C4 the heights of white oaks that are greater than 10 meters tall, use the following commands (you can follow the example by restarting Minitab and entering the data shown after the following example and then filling out the dialog boxes as shown). The parentheses in the command line are used for logical expressions.

Dialog box	**Session command**

Choose **Calc ➤ Mathematical Expressions**	`MTB > LET C3 = ('Species' = 2) AND ('Height' > 10)`
	`MTB > COPY 'Height' C4;`
	`SUBC>   USE C3 = 1.`

Choose **Manip ➤ Copy Columns.**

Click **Use Rows**.

The worksheet looks like this:

C1	C2	C3	C4
Height	Species		
8	2	0	11
11	2	1	14
6	1	0	12
14	2	1	
13	1	0	
10	2	0	
8	1	0	
11	1	0	
12	2	1	
9	1	0	

Row and Column Functions

You can also transform data using **Calc ➤ Functions**. This command lets you create your mathematical expression by selecting from a set of functions that appear in the dialog box. The equivalent session command is still the LET command, used in combination with a number of functions. Appendix A lists all of Minitab's row and column functions. They include, for example, the functions MEAN for mean, SQRT for square root, and MAXI for maximum. To place the cosine of each value in C1 into C10, use the following commands, filling out the dialog box as shown:

Dialog box	Session command
Choose **Calc ➤ Functions.**	MTB > LET C10 = COS(C1)

When you use the LET session command, be sure to put parentheses around the arguments of row and column functions.

Calc ➤ Functions is only useful when you want to evaluate a single function. If you want to evaluate a function in a more complicated expression, you need to use **Calc ➤ Mathematical Expressions**. In this example, you put into C2 the product of 5 plus K1, times the square root of C1.

Dialog box	Session command
Choose **Calc ➤ Mathematical Expressions**. Type C2 in **Variable (new or modified)**, press Tab twice, type (5 + K1) * SQRT(C1) in **Expression**, and then click **OK**.	MTB > LET C2 = (5 + K1) * SQRT(C1)

You can also access a single row of a column. For example, suppose you have sales figures from five different locations stored in C1-C3 for the months January, February, and March of 1992. To put the mean sales value of each month into C4 (rows 1, 2, and 3, respectively), use the following commands (you can follow the example by restarting Minitab and entering the data shown after the example):

Dialog box	Session command
Choose **Calc ➤ Mathematical Expressions**. Type C4 in **Variable (new or modified)**, press Tab, type 1 in **Row number**, press Tab, type MEAN ('JAN') in **Expression**, and then click **OK**.	MTB > LET C4(1) = MEAN('Jan') MTB > LET C4(2) = MEAN('Feb') MTB > LET C4(3) = MEAN('Mar')

This calculates the mean of 'Jan' and places it in the first row of C4. To calculate the means of C2 and C3 and place them in rows 2 and 3, use the Mathematical Expressions dialog box twice more, editing the entries as appropriate.

The worksheet looks like this:

```
C1      C2      C3      C4
Jan     Feb     Mar
43602   36214   41200   45841
45269   40871   42000   39749
46100   42587   42687   41999
44358   43210   45897
49875   35862   38210
```

Precedence of Operations

Calc ➤ Mathematical Expressions computes operations in the following order:

functions and column operations

** (raise to a power)

~ (negation)

* / (multiplication and division)

+ − (addition and subtraction)

comparison operations (greater than, less than, and so on)

& (and)

| (or)

Operations on the same line that have the same precedence are evaluated from left to right. You can always override the default precedence by using parentheses.

Basic Descriptive Statistics

Many data analysts preface a detailed statistical analysis with a look at standard descriptive statistics, including measures like the mean and standard deviation. **Stat ➤ Basic Statistics ➤ Descriptive Statistics**, equivalent to the DESCRIBE session command, displays ten of the most common descriptive statistics.

Descriptive Statistics prints a table of the following basic summary statistics for each column indicated:

N	number of nonmissing observations
N*	number of missing observations (if there are none, Minitab omits this column)
MEAN	average value
MEDIAN	middle value
TRMEAN	a 5% trimmed mean; Minitab removes the smallest 5% and largest 5% and computes the mean of the remaining values
STDEV	sample standard deviation
SEMEAN	standard error of the mean (calculated as STDEV/SQRT(N))
MIN	smallest number
MAX	largest number
Q1	first quartile
Q3	third quartile

You can obtain statistics for a single isolated variable or you can produce separate group statistics for each unique value in the specified column by specifying a **By variable**, equivalent to the BY subcommand. The **By variable** must contain integers from −10,000 to +10,000 or *, the missing value code.

For example, the PULSE.MTW data set described in Chapter 1 contains pulse rates before and after exercise (C1 is before; C2 is after). Column C8 ACTIVITY contains codes for each person's activity level (1 =

slightly active; 2 = moderately active; 3 = very active). To describe the resting pulse (C1 PULSE1) by activity level, use the following commands:

Dialog box	Session command
Choose **Stat ➤ Basic Statistics ➤ Descriptive Statistics**.	MTB > DESCRIBE 'PULSE1'; SUBC> BY 'ACTIVITY'.
Double-click PULSE1 to place it in **Variables**, Click the **By variable** check box, click the corresponding text box, double-click ACTIVITY, and then click **OK**.	

These commands produce the following output:

```
        ACTIVITY      N     MEAN   MEDIAN   TRMEAN   STDEV   SEMEAN
PULSE1         0      1   48.000   48.000   48.000       *        *
               1      9    79.56    82.00    79.56   10.48     3.49
               2     61    72.74    70.00    72.35   10.98     1.41
               3     21    71.57    70.00    71.21    9.63     2.10

        ACTIVITY    MIN      MAX       Q1       Q3
PULSE1         0  48.000   48.000        *        *
               1   62.00    90.00    70.00    90.00
               2   54.00   100.00    65.00    80.00
               3   58.00    92.00    63.00    77.00
```

It appears that as one's activity level increases, one's resting pulse decreases. Those who are slightly active (the 1's) have a mean resting pulse of 79.56. The moderately active (the 2's) are at 72.74, while the very active (the 3's) have a pulse of 71.57. Further analysis could show whether there is evidence that this apparent decrease is significant. (See page 1-6 for an explanation of the activity level of 0.)

Statistical Analysis Commands

The heart of Minitab is its ability to perform a wide range of statistical procedures. This manual describes a few of the more common: t-confidence intervals, t-tests, correlation, regression, analysis of variance, and Minitab's table function with a χ^2 analysis. The limited scope of this manual allows only selected commands to be introduced, accompanied by only a few of the more common subcommands. For a complete listing of Minitab commands and subcommands and their usage syntaxes, refer to Appendix A.

T-Confidence Intervals

To calculate a confidence interval for the mean of one or more variables (assumed to be normally distributed), you use **Stat ➤ Basic Statistics ➤ 1-Sample t**, selecting the **Confidence interval** option. This command is equivalent to the TINTERVAL session command.

Stat ➤ Basic Statistics ➤ 1-Sample t   `TINTERVAL [K% confidence for data in C...C]`

The procedure uses values from the Student's t-distribution. When you use **1-Sample t** to obtain a confidence interval, Minitab assumes an interval size of 95%, unless you enter a different **Level** value (or K session command argument). If you specify a confidence interval less than 1, Minitab assumes it is a confidence coefficient and multiplies it by 100.

For example, using PULSE.MTW, described in Chapter 1, obtain a 95% t-confidence interval for the mean resting pulse of the sample population (contained in column C1 PULSE1):

Dialog box	Session command
Choose **Stat ➤ Basic Statistics ➤ 1-Sample t**.	`MTB > TINTERVAL 'PULSE1'`
Double-click PULSE1 to place it in the **Variables** check box, and then click **OK**.	

These commands produce the following output:

```
              N    MEAN   STDEV  SE MEAN   95.0 PERCENT C.I.
PULSE1       92   72.87   11.01    1.15   ( 70.59,   75.15)
```

Based on this output, you estimate the mean resting pulse to be 72.87, and you can be 95% confident that the upper and lower limits of the reported confidence interval (70.59 and 75.15) cover the true value. An examination of the PULSE.MTW data in Chapter 1 revealed that you might want to look at the confidence interval for each activity group rather than the combined sample.

Paired Data. To compute a confidence interval for paired data, use **Calc ➤ Mathematical Expressions** (equivalent to the LET session command) to store the difference between the two paired columns in a third column. (You could also use the SUBTRACT session command.) Then use **1-Sample t** on that third column.

One-Sample T-Tests

To perform a t-test on one or more variables, use **Stat ➤ Basic Statistics ➤ 1-Sample t**, selecting the **Test mean** option. This command is equivalent to the TTEST session command. If you do not specify the mean μ in the **Test mean** box, Minitab uses μ = 0.

Using PULSE.MTW, described in Chapter 1, perform a t-test on C1 PULSE1 to test whether the mean resting pulse could be equal to 74 (perhaps previous studies tell you that this is the standard mean for the population you are studying):

Dialog box	Session command
Choose **Stat ➤ Basic Statistics ➤ 1-Sample t**.	MTB > TTEST 74.0 'PULSE1'
Double-click PULSE1 to place it in the **Variables** check box.	
Click the **Test mean** option button, double-click the corresponding text box, type 74, and then click **OK**.	

These commands produce the following output:

```
TEST OF MU = 74.000 VS MU N.E. 74.000

              N      MEAN    STDEV   SE MEAN        T   P VALUE
PULSE1       92     72.87    11.01      1.15    -0.98      0.33
```

Minitab reports a p-value of .33. There is insufficient evidence to reject 74.0 as a possible mean resting pulse value.

The t-test output includes the number of observations in the column, the column's mean, standard deviation, and standard error of the mean, the test statistic (T), and the attained significance level (p-value). The p-value is the probability (p) of getting a value as extreme as the computed t-value from a t-distribution with (n−1) degrees of freedom.

Hypothesis Alternatives (ALTERNATIVE). The default t-test setting is two-sided (**not equal** in the **Alternative** box). To perform a one-sided test for the hypothesis μ < K, specify **less than** (or use the Session subcommand ALTERNATIVE = −1). For testing the hypothesis μ > K, specify **greater than** (or use the Session subcommand ALTERNATIVE = 1).

Paired Data. To do a t-test on paired data, use **Calc ➤ Mathematical Expressions** (equivalent to the LET session command) to store the difference between the two paired columns in a third column. (You could also use the SUBTRACT session command.) Then use **1-Sample t** on the new column of differences.

Two-Sample T-Tests

Minitab offers two options for performing two-sample t-tests, both available through **Stat ➤ Basic Statistics ➤ 2-Sample t**. Use the first option, **Samples in one column**, when the data for both groups are in one column (the two groups may be mixed together) and the second column specifies to which group each observation belongs. This option is equivalent to the TWOT session command. Use the second option, **Samples in different columns**, when one sample is in the first column and the second sample is in the second column. This option is equivalent to the TWOSAMPLE session command.

```
Stat ➤ Basic Statistics ➤ 2-Sample t          TWOSAMPLE TEST [K% confidence] for C C
                                                  ALTERNATIVE = K
                                                  POOLED


                                               TWOT [K% confidence] data in C, groups in C
                                                  ALTERNATIVE = K
                                                  POOLED
```

The following example uses **Samples in one column**, but this illustration could equally apply to **Samples in different columns**; the only difference between the two is the form of the data. Minitab calculates a 95% confidence interval for the difference between the population means of the two groups. Minitab assumes the two samples are independent, and that the two populations do not have equal variances. See "Hypothesis Alternatives" in the previous section for information on the test types.

To perform a two-sample t-test on the difference in mean resting pulse rates between genders, using the PULSE.MTW data set described in Chapter 1:

Dialog box	Session command
Choose **Stat ➤ Basic Statistics ➤ 2-Sample t**.	MTB > TWOT 'PULSE1' 'SEX'
Click the **Samples** text box, double-click PULSE1, double-click PULSE2 to place it in the **Subscripts** text box, and then click **OK**.	

These commands produce the following output:

```
TWOSAMPLE T FOR PULSE1
SEX   N     MEAN    STDEV   SE MEAN
1    57     70.42    9.95     1.3
2    35     76.9    11.6      2.0

95 PCT CI FOR MU 1 - MU 2: (-11.2, -1.7)

TTEST MU 1 = MU 2 (VS NE): T = -2.72  P = 0.0084  DF =  63
```

The mean resting pulse for males (1) is 70.42 beats per minute, while for females (2) it is 76.9 beats per minute. The p-value of .0084, which is smaller than the commonly-used α value of .05, suggests that there is a significant difference in mean resting pulse rates between males and females.

Correlation

Stat ➤ Basic Statistics ➤ Correlation, equivalent to the CORRELATION session command, correlates pairs of columns by calculating the Pearson product moment correlation. If you specify more than two columns, Minitab calculates the correlation between every pair of columns and prints the lower triangle of the resulting correlation matrix (in blocks if there is insufficient room to fit across a page).

For example, to correlate the heights of students (HEIGHT) with their weights (WEIGHT) using the PULSE.MTW data set described in Chapter 1, you use the following commands.

Dialog box	Session command
Choose **Stat ➤ Basic Statistics ➤ Correlation**.	`MTB > CORRELATION 'HEIGHT' 'WEIGHT'`
Double-click HEIGHT and then WEIGHT to place them in the **Variables** text box, and then click **OK**.	

These commands produce the following output:

```
Correlation of HEIGHT and WEIGHT = 0.785
```

The correlation value, 0.785, suggests that height and weight are positively correlated. Further tests could explore the significance of this correlation and give you a better idea of the relationship between height and weight. (For example, the correlation and regression examples use the combined male and female data. It may be better to subset the data by gender to see the truer correlation between height and weight.)

The correlation calculation omits any pair of values that have one or both values missing. This is often called "pairwise deletion" of missing values.[1] To calculate Spearman's ρ (rank correlation coefficient), rank both columns using **Manip ➤ Rank** and then use **Correlation** on the columns of ranks.

Regression

Stat ➤ Regression ➤ Regression does simple and multiple regression, using the least squares method to fit a model to one or more predictors. Indicate the response, or y, variable you want to regress, and list all predictor variables in the command statement.

To explore the relationship between weight and height, use the PULSE.MTW data set described in Chapter 1.

Now, perform a regression to examine heights (contained in HEIGHT) based on values of weight (WEIGHT). Store the standardized residuals and the fitted (predicted) values ($\hat{Y}$) in C11 and C12.

Dialog box	Session command
Choose **Stat ➤ Regression ➤ Regression**.	`MTB > NAME C11 'SRES' C12 'FITS'`

Double-click WEIGHT for **Response** and HEIGHT for **Predictors**.	`MTB > REGRESS 'WEIGHT' 1 'HEIGHT';`
	`SUBC>    FITS C11;`
	`SUBC>    SRESIDUALS C12.`

Click the **Standard. resids.** and **Fits** check boxes, and then click **OK**.	

---

1. This method is best for individual correlation, but the correlation matrix as a whole may not be well behaved (for example, it may not be positive definite).

These commands produce the following output:

```
The regression equation is
WEIGHT = - 205 + 5.09 HEIGHT

Predictor        Coef       Stdev     t-ratio          p
Constant      -204.74       29.16       -7.02      0.000
HEIGHT         5.0918      0.4237       12.02      0.000


s = 14.79       R-sq = 61.6%      R-sq(adj) = 61.2%

Analysis of Variance

SOURCE         DF          SS          MS          F          p
Regression      1       31592       31592     144.38      0.000
Error          90       19692         219
Total          91       51284

Unusual Observations
Obs.  HEIGHT    WEIGHT        Fit Stdev.Fit  Residual   St.Resid
  9     72.0    195.00     161.87      2.08     33.13      2.26R
 25     61.0    140.00     105.86      3.62     34.14      2.38R
 40     72.0    215.00     161.87      2.08     53.13      3.63R
 84     68.0    110.00     141.50      1.57    -31.50     -2.14R

R denotes an obs. with a large st. resid.
```

The p-value of .000 suggests that weight is a significant predictor for height, and the R^2 value of 61.6% tells you the amount of variability in the response that this model accounts for.

In a simple regression, **Stat ► Regression ► Regression** prints the regression equation, a table listing the coefficient, standard deviation, t-ratio, and p-value for each variable in the model. The output then lists s (the estimated standard deviation about the regression line), R^2 (the coefficient of determination), and R^2 adjusted for degrees of freedom, followed by an analysis of variance table.

You can store many diagnostics for further analysis (see Appendix A for the complete subcommand list). To store the residuals and predicted values (fits), list two empty columns at the end of the command line. If you specify one column, Minitab stores the standardized residuals in it; if you specify a second, Minitab stores the fitted values in it. You can then use these columns to do residual plots and to plot the $\hat{Y}$'s (the fitted values).

Minitab also marks unusual observations with an X if the predictor is unusual, or with an R if the residual is unusual. For information on how Minitab determines unusual observations, check the on-line Help topic corresponding to the Regression dialog box.

Prediction Intervals for New Observations (PREDICT). (Release 9 and up).To compute fitted values based on the regression equation for given values of the predictors, click **Options** in the Regression dialog box, then enter the constants or columns in the **Prediction intervals for new observations** box, equivalent to the PREDICT subcommand. You can list one constant for each predictor or a list of columns, one for each predictor. If you want to list multiple rows of new predictor values without storing them in a column, use the session command REGRESS, which allows multiple PREDICT subcommands (up to ten).

Minitab prints a table that includes the fitted values, their standard deviations, a 95% confidence interval, and a 95% prediction interval. A prediction interval gives an interval for the predicted value of a single observation, while a confidence interval gives the interval for the mean of all y values corresponding to a given value of x.

Fitting a Regression Line (%FITLINE). You can fit a regression line quickly and easily with the Minitab macro **Stat ➤ Regression ➤ Fitted Line Plot** (%FITLINE). The sample sessions in Chapters 1 and 2 illustrate how to use this command (menu users, see page 1-19; session users, see page 2-14).

Analysis of Variance

The **Stat ➤ ANOVA ➤ Oneway** and **Stat ➤ ANOVA ➤ Oneway (Unstacked)** commands compute a one-way analysis of variance. **Oneway (Unstacked)** requires that the data for each group be in a separate column, while **Oneway** expects that all the data are in one column, with a second column giving the levels (subscripts or group identification). These commands correspond to the ONEWAY and AOVONEWAY session commands.

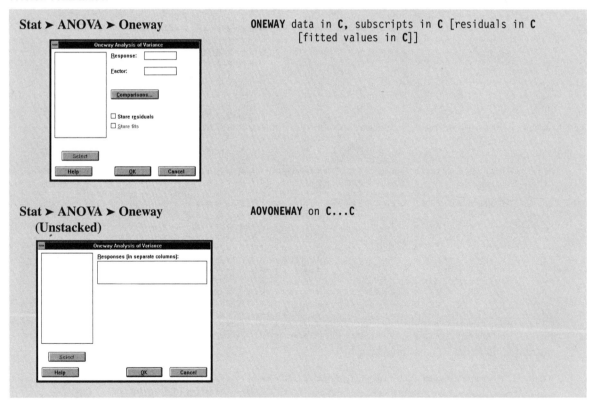

Using the PULSE.MTW data set described in Chapter 1, look at a one-way analysis of variance for resting pulse (C1 PULSE1) and activity level (C8 ACTIVITY). The **Oneway** command will serve as an example in this manual. Minitab stores residuals, or data minus fits, in an optional third column. It can also store fits, or level means, in an optional fourth column. The levels must be integers between −10,000 and 10,000 or the missing value ∗.

Dialog box	**Session command**
Choose **Stat ➤ ANOVA ➤ Oneway**.	MTB > ONEWAY 'PULSE1' 'ACTIVITY'
Double-click PULSE1 for **Response** and ACTIVITY for **Factor**, and then click **OK**.	

These commands produce the following output:

```
ANALYSIS OF VARIANCE ON PULSE1
SOURCE     DF       SS       MS        F        p
ACTIVITY    3     1057      352     3.11    0.030
ERROR      88     9971      113
TOTAL      91    11028
                                INDIVIDUAL 95 PCT CI'S FOR MEAN
                                BASED ON POOLED STDEV
  LEVEL     N     MEAN    STDEV   -------+---------+---------+---------
      0     1    48.00     0.00   (----------*----------)
      1     9    79.56    10.48                          (---*--)
      2    61    72.74    10.98                       (*-)
      3    21    71.57     9.63                     (--*-)
                                  -------+---------+---------+---------
POOLED STDEV =    10.64                 40        60        80
```

To test the null hypothesis that mean resting pulse is the same regardless of activity level, compare Minitab's p-value of .03 with the commonly-used α level of .05. Because the p-value is smaller than .05, reject the null hypothesis and surmise that mean resting pulse rates may differ significantly for different activity levels.

Minitab's Table Function

Stat ➤ Tables ➤ Cross Tabulation, equivalent to the TABLE session command, prints one-way, two-way, and multi-way tables of categorical data. The cells may contain counts, percents, and statistics from a χ^2 test. They may also contain summary statistics such as means, standard deviations, and maximums for associated variables. **Cross Tabulation** uses two types of variables: *classification variables*, listed on the command line, which determine the cells of the table, and *associated variables*, listed on the subcommand lines, which calculate the functions you specify for each unique classification or cell defined in the table. Minitab calculates statistics, such as a mean or minimum, for these variables. You may specify up to 10 classification variables, each containing integers between −10,000 and +10,000 or the missing value ∗. The values need not be consecutive.

The following example uses PULSE.MTW (the data set from Chapter 1), and generates a table that shows the relationship between those who smoke (C4 SMOKES) and their activity level (C8 ACTIVITY). In this example, the **Column percents** option (equivalent to the COLPERCENTS Session subcommand) is selected so that the output gives the percentage of the entire column that the count represents.

Dialog box	**Session command**

Choose **Stat ➤ Tables ➤ Cross Tabulation**.

Double-click SMOKES and ACTIVITY for **Classification variables**, click the **Column percents** check box, and then click **OK**.

```
MTB > TABLE 'SMOKES' 'ACTIVITY';
SUBC>    COLPERCENTS.
```

These commands produce the following output:

```
ROWS: SMOKES     COLUMNS: ACTIVITY

              0        1        2        3      ALL

    1    100.00    33.33    31.15    23.81    30.43
    2       --     66.67    68.85    76.19    69.57
  ALL    100.00   100.00   100.00   100.00   100.00

  CELL CONTENTS --
               % OF COL
```

This table summarizes the number and percentage of smokers at each activity level. The 1's represent those who smoke regularly while the 2's are those who do not. A third of the inactive students smoke while only a fourth of the very active smoke. Further analysis would be necessary to test whether there is evidence that this is a significant difference. (Chapter 1 accounts for the activity level of 0.)

The values in the first column specified in the command line are the rows of the table, and the values in the second column are the columns. **Cross Tabulation** produces a separate table for every possible combination of values from the remaining columns listed in the command line.

Displaying Summaries. Click the **Summaries** button to produce various summary statistics for each cell of the table. For example, you can click **Means** to display the means for each cell, or **Data** to list all of the data in each cell. These correspond to the MEANS and DATA Session subcommands.

Chisquare Test of Independence (CHISQUARE). Click the **Chisquare analysis** check box to test the independence (or homogeneity) of the row and column variables in a two-way table. This corresponds to the CHISQUARE session command. Minitab always prints the value of the χ^2 statistic, and you select one of three options: **Show count**, which displays the counts, **Above and expected count**, which displays the counts and expected counts, or **Above and std. residual**, which displays the counts, expected counts, and standardized residuals. These options corresponds to $K = 1$, $K = 2$, and $K = 3$ with the CHISQUARE Session subcommand.

This example shows a χ^2 analysis of gender and activity level from the PULSE.MTW data set. The CHISQUARE 3 subcommand tells Minitab to use the third level of output.

Dialog box	Session command
Choose **Stat ➤ Tables ➤ Cross Tabulation**.	`MTB > TABLE 'Sex' 'Activity';`
Double-click SEX and ACTIVITY for **Classification variables**, click the **Chisquare analysis** check box, click the **Above and std. residual** option button, and then click **OK**.	`SUBC>   CHISQUARE 3.`

These commands produce the following output:

```
     ROWS: SEX     COLUMNS: ACTIVITY

               0       1       2       3     ALL

   1       1       5      35      16      57
        0.62    5.58   37.79   13.01   57.00
        0.48   -0.24   -0.45    0.83     --

   2       0       4      26       5      35
        0.38    3.42   23.21    7.99   35.00
       -0.62    0.31    0.58   -1.06     --

  ALL      1       9      61      21      92
        1.00    9.00   61.00   21.00   92.00
         --      --      --      --      --

 CHI-SQUARE =    3.118   WITH D.F. =    3
     CELL CONTENTS --
                    COUNT
                    EXP FREQ
                    STD RES
```

You can also use the **Chisquare analysis** option, which gives a summary χ^2 statistic (in this case, 3.118), to compare with percentiles from the χ^2 distribution using **Calc ➤ Probability Distributions ➤ Chisquare**, equivalent to the INVCDF session command. See Appendix A and on-line Help for information on Minitab's distribution commands.

6
Graphics

- Minitab Graphics Modes
- Scatter Plots
- Histograms
- Boxplots
- Control Charts
- Saving and Printing Graphs
- Other Graphics Options

Minitab Graphics Modes

Minitab offers a number of different graph types for plotting single and multiple variables and for producing statistical control charts. There are two modes available, *low-* and *high-resolution*. While both modes display the same information, the high-resolution mode accommodates pictorial elements like lines and colors and looks better for presentation.

Low-resolution graphs are called *character graphs* and are made up of normal keyboard characters. You can view character-based graphs on any screen, print them on any printer, and store them in an outfile. This example shows a high-resolution histogram and a character histogram of the heights of students in a class. Notice that the information is the same; it is just displayed differently.]

High-resolution histogram   **Character histogram**

```
Histogram of HEIGHT    N = 92

Midpoint   Count
      62       7   *******
      64       6   ******
      66      13   *************
      68      17   *****************
      70      17   *****************
      72      15   ***************
      74      14   **************
      76       3   ***
```

If you are using menus, you choose the Graph menu commands to create high-resolution graphs and the Character Graphs submenu commands to create low-resolution graphs, as shown here (for Release 8, character and high-resolution graphs are on the same dialogs):

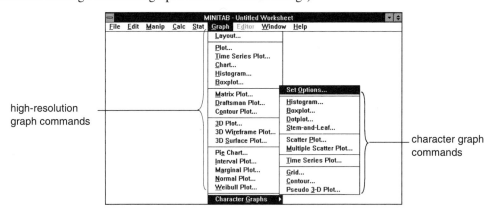

If you are using session commands, you can switch back and forth between character graphs and high-resolution graphs by typing the commands GSTD (short for Graph Standard; sets the mode to character) and GPRO (short for Graph Professional; sets the mode to high-resolution). Minitab automatically starts in high-resolution graph mode, so if you typed the HISTOGRAM command, Minitab would produce a high-resolution histogram. However, if you wanted a character histogram, you would first switch to character graph mode by typing GSTD and then HISTOGRAM. Any subsequent graph command you execute produces a character graph until you type GPRO to switch back to high-resolution mode. GSTD and GPRO work like toggles: you turn one on and it stays on until you turn the other on. The examples in this chapter show only high-resolution graphs.

There are a few exceptions for session command users. If you are using a mainframe version of release 9 standard or releases 6, 7, or 8, you produce high-resolution graphs not with the GSTD and GPRO toggles but by typing the letter G before a graph command. For example, HISTOGRAM produces a character histogram while GHISTOGRAM produces a high-resolution histogram. The G-style high-resolution commands are not shown separately in this chapter, but you can add a G in front of the character commands shown to make the equivalent G-style graph. Check on-line Help or see your System Administrator for more information on how you should produce high-resolution graphs. The Release 8 graphics dialogs look different from those shown in this chapter, but the directions still work.

Minitab also offers a wide variety of graph customization subcommands and dialog box options. See *Other Graphics Options* on page 6-9 for more information about the options you have when creating graphs in Minitab.

Scatter Plots

Scatter plots help you to investigate the relationship between two variables, like weight and height, or diameter and volume. The first column you specify is the vertical (y) axis (usually a dependent variable) and the second is the horizontal (x) axis (usually an independent variable).

To plot weight against height for the PULSE.MTW data set described in Chapter 1 and give the plot a title, use the following commands:

Dialog box	Session command

Choose **Graph ➤ Plot**.

Double-click **WEIGHT** as the Y variable and **HEIGHT** as the X variable.

Click the **Annotation** down arrow and click **Title**.

```
MTB > PLOT 'WEIGHT' * 'HEIGHT';
SUBC>   TITLE 'Weight versus Height'.
```

(Character and G-style high-resolution graphs)
```
MTB > PLOT 'WEIGHT' 'HEIGHT';
SUBC>   TITLE 'Weight versus Height'.
```

Type **Weight versus Height** in the Title box and click **OK** twice.

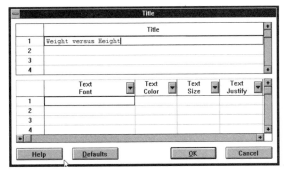

These commands produce the following graph:

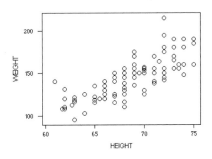

Histograms

The Histogram command plots a separate histogram for each column. Minitab divides the data into intervals and displays a bar representing each interval. The height of the bar corresponds to the number of observations in the interval. Observations falling on an interval boundary go in the interval with the larger midpoint.

Graph ➤ Histogram   **HISTOGRAM C**

To plot a histogram of the resting pulses of a set of students using the PULSE.MTW data set described in Chapter 1, use the following commands:

Dialog box	**Session command**
Choose **Graph ➤ Histogram**.	MTB > HIST 'WEIGHT'
Double-click **PULSE1** as the X variable, and then click **OK**.	

These commands produce the following graph:

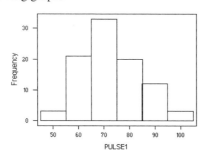

The histogram shows a generally normal distribution.

Boxplots

The Boxplot command prints a boxplot (also called a box-and-whisker plot) that displays the main features of a data set and permits simple comparisons of several batches of data. A default boxplot consists of a box, whiskers, and outliers. Minitab draws a line across the box at the median. The bottom of the box is at the first quartile and the top is at the third quartile, so the box represents the middle half of the data. The whiskers are the lines that extend from the top and bottom of the box, indicating the extent of the data. Outliers are points outside the whiskers, plotted with asterisks (*).

Graph ➤ Boxplot

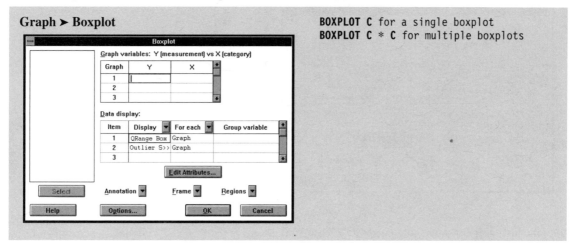

BOXPLOT C for a single boxplot
BOXPLOT C * C for multiple boxplots

To plot a boxplot of students' resting pulses by gender, using the PULSE data, use the following commands:

Dialog box	Session command
Choose **Graph ➤ Boxplot**.	`MTB > BOXP 'PULSE1' * 'SEX'`
Double-click **PULSE1** as the Y variable and **SEX** as the X variable.	For a character plot, type:
Click **OK**.	`MTB > BOXP 'PULSE1';` `SUBC>   BY SEX.`

These commands produce the following graph:

The males (coded as 1) have a lower median resting pulse rate than the females (coded as 2). Further investigation could explore the significance of this.

Control Charts

Minitab offers a number of different statistical process control (SPC) charts to study the variation in a process over a period of time. These charts plot a summary statistic (for example, a sample mean or sample proportion) against the sample number, and draw the following three lines on the chart:

1. Center line: the estimate of the average value of the summary statistic.

2. Upper control limit (UCL): by default, drawn 3 standard deviation limits above the center line.

3. Lower control limit (LCL): by default, drawn 3 standard deviation limits below the center line.

When a process is in control, it is unlikely that points will fall outside the control limits (the chances are about 3 in a thousand). You might want to investigate further if points do fall outside the control limits. Minitab's Xbar command produces an $\overline{X}$ chart, one of the most common statistical process control charts. The rest of this section describes its use. The other SPC charts operate in a similar manner.

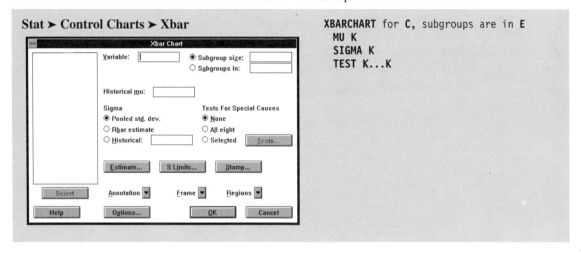

The Xbar command displays a separate chart for each column. Each column contains data from a single process. E specifies the subgroups (also called samples). If E is a constant, say 5, then Minitab takes the first 5 rows as the first sample, the second 5 rows as the second sample, and so on. If E is a column, then the subscripts in that column determine the subgroups.

Minitab calculates and plots the mean of all the observations in each subgroup, plotting up to 60 means on one chart. It draws additional charts if necessary.

Specifying Parameters. Minitab assumes that observations come from a normal distribution with mean μ and standard deviation σ. You can specify these parameters in the Xbar Chart dialog box or using the session subcommands MU and SIGMA. The Xbar command uses the value of μ for the center line and σ for the upper and lower control limits. If you do not specify them, Minitab estimates them from the data.

Tests for Special Causes. You can select one or more of the eight tests for special causes in the Xbar Chart dialog box or using the session subcommand TEST. Each test detects a specific pattern in the data plotted on the chart. The occurrence of a pattern suggests a special cause for variation, one that should be investigated. Subgroup sizes must be equal. When a point fails a test, Minitab marks it with the test number on the plot. If a point fails more than one test, Minitab prints the number of the first failed test, and a summary table with complete information.

For example, a company that manufactures metal washers wants to monitor washer dimensions to ensure better quality. The company measured the inside diameters of samples of washers and entered the data into C1. To produce an $\overline{X}$ chart to monitor whether the process is in control, you can enter the data shown and then use the following commands:

Dialog box	Session command
Type the data shown to the right into C1 of the Data window.	MTB > SET C1
	DATA> 12.0 12.3 12.1 11.8 12.0 11.1 12.7
	DATA> 12.2 12.4 12.6 12.0 12.4
Choose **Stat ➤ Control Charts ➤ Xbar**.	DATA> 12.5 12.1 12.7 12.5 12.3 12.2 11.9 11.9
Double-click **C1** as the Variable.	DATA> 12.1 11.6 11.7 11.9
	DATA> 12.9 12.9 12.8 11.7 12.8 11.1
Click the **Subgroup size** text box and type **3**.	DATA> END
	MTB > XBAR C1 3;
Click the **All eight** option button under Tests for Special Causes.	SUBC> TITLE 'X-bar Chart for Inside Diameter';
	SUBC> TEST 1:8.
Click the **Annotation** down arrow and then click **Title**.	
Type **X-bar Chart for Inside Diameter** in the Title box and click **OK** twice.	

These commands produce the following graph:

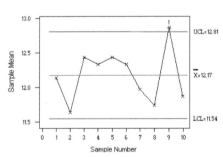

The chart shows that the process is not under control, because one point falls outside the control limits, and Minitab reports that the process failed Test 1, which means that the point is beyond the upper control limit.

Saving and Printing Graphs

If you use menus and dialog boxes, to save a Graph window, or any window, in Minitab, use the **File ➤ Save Window As** command. It opens a dialog box similar to the **Save Worksheet As** dialog box described earlier in this guide.

Be sure the Graph window is the active window (its title bar will be highlighted). Choose **File ➤ Save Window As**. Type an appropriate name in the File Name box (or the Save As box for the Macintosh), select the directory you want, and then click OK. Your graph is now saved in an .MGF file, short for Minitab Graphics Format. You can reopen the file in Minitab any time you want.

If you use session commands and you want to save a graph, use the GSAVE subcommand, followed by the file name in quotes. For commands that generate more than one graph, Minitab uses the file name you specify and saves each graph in a separate file, appending the file name with a three-digit number (001, 002, and so on).

You can save character-based graphs in the same way you would save other Minitab output using an outfile (see Chapter 4). For example, to save and print a character histogram, start an outfile and then instruct Minitab to plot the histogram:

```
MTB > OUTFILE 'MYGRAPH'
MTB > HISTOGRAM C1
MTB > NOOUTFILE
```

The file MYGRAPH.LIS now contains a histogram of the first column. An outfile is a text (ASCII) file that can be edited by any word processor and printed on any printer.

To print a graph, if you are using menus, be sure the Graph window is the active window (its title bar will be highlighted). Choose **File ➤ Print Window**, and then click OK. On mainframe versions of Release 9, use the command GPRINT after saving the graph with GSAVE.

Other Graphics Options

This chapter has shown only the very basic steps you take to produce graphs in Minitab. You can customize Minitab graphs in almost an unlimited number of ways. The dialog boxes you have seen in this chapter contain features that help you customize your graphs; each of these features corresponds to a session command, which you can find in Appendix A. For example:

- The Data display table lets you define how the data values look on the graph.

- The Edit Attributes button lets you specify how you want the data values displayed on the graph.

- The Annotation, Frame, and Regions buttons let you control the supplementary information on a graph, like its title, its color, its legend, and so on.

- Most graph dialog boxes have an Options button that controls options specific to the graph type you are working with.

In Minitab Release 10 and later, you can edit graphs, adding/eliminating text and other elements in order to quickly customize your graph. You can also brush graphs to identify which row points on a graph correspond to.

If you are using session commands, see on-line Help for the graphics subcommands that give you full graphics functionality. Many of the subcommands have additional subcommands. The more time you spend making graphs with Minitab, the more options you will discover, and the more you can make your graphs look exactly the way you want them to.

Appendix A:
Abridged Quick Reference

s Quick Reference contains brief descriptions of most Minitab commands and features. The reference is divided two sections.

ction 1: For Macintosh and Windows (page 2)

s section is for users of the Macintosh and Windows versions of Minitab. This section tells you about:

- Using Menus and Dialog Boxes
- Using Minitab Windows, like the Session window
- Creating, Editing, Brushing, and Saving Graphs
- Using Keyboard Shortcuts

ess noted, all features in section 1 are available in Release 8 for Macintosh or later, and Release 9 for Windows or r. Features that were added in later releases are signified with a symbol. See the Feature Key below.

ction 2: Command Reference (page 9)

sion commands can be used in every release of Minitab, including the versions that provide menus and dialog es. This section of the Quick Reference describes each command in the following areas:

- Basic Commands
- Statistics
- Quality Control
- DOE
- Graphics
- Macros

ess noted, each command is available for all versions of Minitab, from Release 7 or later, on all platforms: DOS, ndows, Macintosh, Unix, etc. Features that were added in later releases are signified with a symbol. See the ture Key Below.

ature Key

nmands added in later releases of Minitab are signified like this:

available in Release 8 or later
available in Release 9 or later
available in Release 9 for Windows and Release 9 Enhanced for VAX/VMS or later
available in Release 10 or later
available in Release 10*Xtra* or later

Section 1: For Macintosh and Windows

Typographical Conventions

- **File ➤ Open Worksheet** means Click **File** in the menu bar, then click **Open Worksheet**.
- Ctrl+M means while holding the Ctrl key, press the M key.
- ⊖ denotes mouse instructions.

Sample Dialog Box

The variable list box shows the available columns for the current text box.

This text box takes one column.

This text box can contain more than one column.

Buttons with "..." following their name open a subdialog box.

Command buttons perform some action immediately.

Click this to get Help on the dialog box.

Select one or more check boxes to choose options.

Resetting Dialog Box Defaults

When you open a dialog box, you will notice that Minitab "remembers" all of its settings from the last time you used it in your session. (You must have actually executed the command.) This saves time if you use some of the same settings again.

When you want to clear the previous settings and return a dialog box to its default state:

- Microsoft Windows: Press F3, or choose ⊟ (the control menu box) and select **Reset Defaults**.
- Macintosh: Choose **Edit ➤ Reset Defaults**, or press ⌘+R.

When you return a dialog box to its default state, all of the subdialog boxes also return to their defaults.

Edit Last Command Dialog Feature

When you want to recall the last dialog box you used in your current Minitab session, choose **Edit ➤ Edit Last Command Dialog** or

- Microsoft Windows: Press Ctrl+E.
- Macintosh: Press ⌘+E.

Working with Minitab Windows

(for Microsoft Windows)

To...	Do This...
Switch between Minitab windows	Click on any visible window area; double-click on any visible window icon; or choose **Window ➤ Data/Session/History/Info/Name of graph**.
Minimize a window	Click the ▼ button.
Minimize all windows	Choose **Window ➤ Minimize All**.
Maximize a window	Click the ▲ button.
Restore a window to its previous size	Click the ⬍ button.
Close a Graph window	Double-click ⊟ (the control menu) or choose **Close** from the control menu.
Close all Graph windows	Choose **Window ➤ Close All Graphs**.
Move windows or dialog boxes	Position the mouse pointer on the title bar, then drag to new location.
Size a window	Point to any part of the window border. When the mouse pointer turns into a two-sided arrow ↔, drag the border to the size you want.
Get different views of your windows	Choose **Window ➤ Cascade** or **Window ➤ Tile**.

(for Macintosh)

To...	Do This...
Switch between Minitab windows	Click on any visible window area, or choose **Window ➤ Data/Session/History/Info/Name of graph**.
Hide a window	Choose **Window ➤ Hide Window**, or click on the Close box in the upper-left corner of the window.
Hide all windows	Choose **Window ➤ Hide All Windows**.
Move a window to the back	Choose **Window ➤ Move Window To Back**.
Make a window full size	Click on the zoom box at the right end of a small window's title bar.
Make a window small	Click on the zoom box at the right end of a full window's title bar.
Close a Graph window	Choose **Window ➤ Close Graph**.
Close all Graph windows	Choose **Window ➤ Close All Graphs**.
Move windows or dialog boxes	Position the mouse pointer on the title bar, then drag to a new location.
Size a window	Point to the size box in the lower-right corner of the window, and drag vertically to change the height; horizontally to change the width; or diagonally to change both dimensions. Release the mouse button when the outline reaches the size you want.

ssion Window Overview

Session window commands that you type in at the active prompt or in the Command Line Editor, or that are generated when you use dialog boxes.

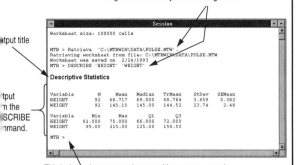

tput title

tput n the SCRIBE nmand.

This is the active command prompt. You can type session commands directly on this line or generate them by using dialog boxes or the Command Line Editor.

sing Session Commands

can type session commands in two places: the Session window and the Command Editor.

ssion Window

Type commands at the MTB> prompt, subcommands at the SUBC> prompt, and data at the DATA> prompt.

Execute commands or insert blank lines (you can change these defaults): ⑩

	To Execute a Command	To Insert a Blank Line
Microsoft Windows:	Enter	Ctrl + Enter
Macintosh	return	⌘ + return

If you are unable to type commands in the Session window, command language may be disabled. See *Disabling & Enabling Command Language* on page 3. ⑩

mmand Line Editor ⑩

Open the Editor with **Edit ➤ Command Line Editor** or keyboard shortcut (page 8)

Type commands at the cursor, then click **Submit Commands** to execute them.

Execute commands or insert blank lines (you can change these defaults):

	To Execute a Command	To Insert a Blank Line
Microsoft Windows:	Ctrl + Enter	Enter
Macintosh	⌘ + return	return

Use the Command Line Editor to execute commands used previously in your session:

–Highlight commands in the Session or History windows, then open the Command Line Editor. The highlighted commands appear in the editing window.

–Or, while the Session or History window is active, choose **Edit ➤ Select All**. When you open the Editor, all commands used in your current session will appear in the editing window. Since it is so easy to delete and edit commands in the editing window, this is a quick way to re-execute commands.

You can cut, copy, and paste to and from the Command Line Editor, word processors, spreadsheets, and Minitab windows—including the Data window.

aking Output Editable or Read-Only ⑩

Session window is by default set to Read-Only. This means that output can be ied, but it cannot be deleted or modified.

To set the Session window to Editable, choose **Editor ➤ Make Output Editable**. If the Editor menu says **Make Output Read-Only**, you do not have to do anything.

To set the Session window to Read-Only, choose **Editor ➤ Make Output Read-Only**. If the Editor menu says **Make Output Editable**, you do not have to do anything.

Disabling & Enabling Command Language ⑩

You can hide all commands generated by dialog boxes and the Command Line Editor, and suppress all command and data prompts, by choosing **Editor ➤ Disable Command Language**. Choose **Editor ➤ Enable Command Language** to restore the active command prompt and to display all subsequent commands.

Next Command and Previous Command ⑩

■ Choose **Editor ➤ Next Command** to move forward to the next output section in the Session window.

■ Choose **Editor ➤ Previous Command** to move backward by output section.

Saving Session Window Contents

Session window contents are separate from your worksheet, and are not saved when you choose **File ➤ Save Worksheet**. The Session window can hold up to 15,000 lines of text before output "overflows" to a file or is discarded, as you choose. You can save the session contents to an ASCII text file that you can print or edit further in a word processor. ASCII files do not contain any of the fonts that you see in the Session window.

■ **Save manually at any time.** With the Session window active, choose **File ➤ Save Window As**, type a name in **File Name**, and click **OK**.

■ **Save automatically.** Change your preferences see below so that when you exit Minitab or overflow the Session window, Minitab will automatically (a) save the session contents to a file, (b) prompt you to save to a file, or (c) discard session contents.

To change your preferences for how to save Session window contents, choose:
Microsoft Windows: **Edit ➤ Save Preferences ➤ Session Window**
Macintosh: **Edit ➤ Save Preferences ➤ Session Window Full** ⑩

■ **Record a Session**. Use the **File ➤ Other Files ➤ Start Recording Session** (OUTFILE) command to generate an outfile with an LIS extension. This file contains all the Session window output (but not any comments you may have added) from the time the command is invoked until you exit Minitab or use the **File ➤ Other Files ➤ Stop Recording Session** (NOOUTFILE) command.

Saving, Printing, and Producing Reports

Make the specified window active by clicking in the window or choosing **Window ➤** the window name. Then:

Active Window	To...	Do this
Session	save your analysis as a text (ASCII) file	Choose **File ➤ Save Window As**.
	print the entire Session window contents	Choose **File ➤ Print Window**.
	print just a part of the Session window	Highlight the section, then choose Microsoft Windows: **File ➤ Print Window ➤ Selection** Macintosh: **File ➤ Print Selection**
Data	print the entire Data window contents	Choose **File ➤ Print Window**.
	print just a part of the Data window	Highlight the section, then choose Microsoft Windows: **File ➤ Print Window ➤ Selection** Macintosh: **File ➤ Print Selection**
Graph	save your graph as a Minitab Graphics Format (MGF) file	Choose **File ➤ Save Window As**.
	print the Graph window	Choose **File ➤ Print Window**.
Any	save all your data as a Minitab worksheet	Choose **File ➤ Save Worksheet** or **File ➤ Save Worksheet As**.
	save your data as a portable worksheet (all data), or as a text file or other format (constants and matrices are not saved).	Choose **File ➤ Save Worksheet As** and pick one of the file types from the **List Files of Type** box.

Graphs ⑨E

A Graph window contains a single high-resolution graph.

A Simple Plot with a Title

1. Choose **File ➤ Open Worksheet**, choose *market.mtw* from the *Data* subdirectory, and click **OK**.

2. Choose **Graph ➤ Plot**.

3. Fill in the **Graph variables** table as shown. Select column names for the y-axis and x-axis variables by double-clicking the names in the variable list box. You could produce a graph clicking **OK** or continue to add a title.

Put the x- and y-variables for the graph in this table. For simple plots, just fill in **Y** and **X** with y- and x-variables and click **OK**.

Pop-up menus give you more choices. In a table, when you make a choice from a pop-up menu, all selected cells get that choice.

This table tells how data points look on the graph. Use this table when you want to do things like connect the points, or display the points as areas.

Clicking this button brings up a dialog box that lets you edit the appearance of the elements in the active row of the **Data display** table.

4. To put a title on the graph, choose **Annotation ➤ Title** and type the title as shown. (Move to any other cell to display the text values at the bottom of the dialog box.)

5. Click **OK** in both dialog boxes to produce the graph.

se **File ➤ Save Window As** from an active Graph window to save a graph in a
b Graphics Format (MGF) file. You can open an MGF file in your next Minitab
n. See also *Exporting Graphs to Other Applications* on page 7.

Graph windows by choosing **Window ➤ Close All Graphs**.

references in **Edit ➤ Save Preferences ➤ Graphics** determine how Minitab
when you close graphs or when you have too many graphs. Click **Help** in the
ics Preferences dialog box for more information.

Graph Brushing ⑩

This is a brushed region. Points in this region are
highlighted, and show up on the Brushing palette, allowing
you to compare different characteristics visually.

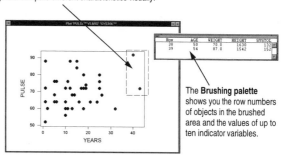

The **Brushing palette**
shows you the row numbers
of objects in the brushed
area and the values of up to
ten indicator variables.

To...	Do this
enter brushing mode	Choose **Editor ➤ Brush**.
add identifier variables to the Brushing palette	Choose **Editor ➤ Set ID Variables**, click **Use columns**, type the columns you wish to use as identifier variables, and select **Use as default for all graphs** or **Use for this graph only**.
brush points (form a new brushing region)	While in brushing mode, move the mouse until the pointed hand tool ☞ appears, then drag until the new brushing region is the size you want.
move an existing brushing region	Move the mouse on top of the existing brushing region. When it turns into an open hand ☜, you can drag the brushing region to a different position.
add additional points to the Brushing palette	If you press (Shift) while you are moving the brushing region, you add the points that the brushing region passes over while keeping the brushed points you had. or (Shift)+click on points you want to add individually.
brush a single point	Click the point.
select brushed points for editing	While points are brushed, choose **Editor ➤ Edit**.
brush across Graph windows	For each graph you want to include: make the graph active (by clicking on it), then choose **Editor ➤ Brush** to make the graph brushable.
display/hide row numbers on the Brushing palette	Choose **Editor ➤ Set ID Variables**, check or uncheck **Use row numbers**.
display the Brushing palette	Choose **Editor ➤ Show Brushing Palette**.
hide the Brushing Palette	Click once on the close box at the top left of the Brushing palette or Choose **Editor ➤ Hide Brushing Palette**.
resize the Brushing palette vertically	Drag the top, bottom, or corners of the Brushing palette as desired.
move the Brushing palette	Drag the Brushing palette by the title bar.
highlight a graph point from the Brushing palette	Click on a row on the Brushing palette.
highlight many graph points from the Brushing palette	Drag the rows you want to highlight on the Brushing palette, or (*for Microsoft Windows...*) (Shift)+🖱 to highlight contiguous rows or (Ctrl)+🖱 to add/delete individual rows to/from the current selection (*for Macintosh...*) Click other rows to highlight the points, then click again to delete from the selection.
brush multiple graphs	Brush the points in one graph. The points automatically highlight in other graphs that support brushing.

Graph Editing—Double-Click a Graph to Start ⑩—all Graph Editing features

To enter edit mode, double-click on a Graph window, or from an active Graph window, choose **Editor ➤ Edit**. If the Tool or Attribute palettes do not display, choose **Editor ➤ Show Palette** and **Editor ➤ Show Attribute Palette**. For descriptions of the editing palettes, see the back cover.

Drawing Objects and Adding Text on a Graph

You draw objects, or add text to a graph, by selecting the tool you want from the Tool palette, then drawing on the graph. If you press ⟨Shift⟩ *after* you depress the mouse button, yc draw lines or polylines along the nearest 45-degree line. This is especially helpful when you want to draw (or move) an object only horizontally, only vertically, or an equal distance horizontally and vertically. To draw multiple objects with the same attributes, refer to Help or the *MINITAB Reference Manual.*

Selecting Existing Objects and Text

To select a graph object, click ⟨↖⟩, the selection tool on the Tool palette, then click the object on the graph. You can select objects even if you make them invisible. You must click edge line to select hollow polygons, that is, polygons that have no fill (the default fill is solid white for objects that you draw). Selected objects have handles that appear as follows:

When you select symbols, they display two handles.

Text strings have handles at vertices (corners) and at line midpoints of a rectangle that surrounds them.

Unrotated rectangles, squares, ellipses, and circles have handles at vertices (corners) and at line midpoints. For circles and ellipses, the vertices and endpoints are located on a rectangle that surrounds the object.

Some handles on a selected polygon. Selected polygons have handles at each vertex.

Selecting Multiple Objects and Text

All of the following start with ⟨↖⟩, the selection tool, active:

Select items one at a time, object by object,	⟨Shift⟩+click	While holding down ⟨Shift⟩, click on each item you wish to select.
Select all objects in a rectangular area—including all objects that extend even *partially* into the rectangular area	Drag	Move the mouse to an empty place on the graph, and outline the area by dragging diagonally from corner to corner. When you begin to drag, the cursor turns into a ⟨⟩ and a dashed rectangle indicates the extent of the selection area while you are dragg
Add an item to a current selection	⟨Shift⟩+click	While holding down ⟨Shift⟩, click on each item you wish to add to the current selection
Add all objects in another rectangular area to a current selection	⟨Shift⟩+drag	While holding down ⟨Shift⟩, go to an empty place on the graph, outline the area by dra from corner to corner diagonally. When you begin to drag, the cursor turns into a ⟨⟩ and a dashed rectangle indicates the extent of the selection area while you are dragg
Select all objects on a graph	⟨Ctrl⟩+⟨A⟩ (Microsoft Windows) ⟨⌘⟩+⟨A⟩ (Macintosh)	Choose **Edit ➤ Select All**.

Aligning Objects

You can align objects on a graph with other objects in a selection, or with the page (the page corresponds to the selectable area of the Graph window).

Editor ➤ Align brings up the Align dialog box.

To show alignment, the examples below use this arrangement of elements:

When you choose **Editor ➤ Align ➤ Align with page**, entire selection aligns relative to the associated clipping regions. Because objects align with their associated clipp regions when you choose **Align with page**, you may encounter results that seem unexpected. Use **Edit ➤ Ur** necessary to return to the initial arrangement.

You can check both **Align horizontally** and **Align vertically** to do both at the same time.

Align with each other ➤ Align horizontally (with Align vertically unchecked) ➤			Align with each other ➤ Align vertically (with Align horizontally unchecked) ➤		
Left	Center	Right	Top	Center	Bottom
A text string	A text string	A text string	A text string	A text string	A text string

Symbols are treated as points and are always aligned by their centers, not their edges. Text strings are aligned by their text area extent, not by the exact space that the text appear

~ving Objects and Text

~ing with the Mouse

~ove an object or text string, click ▲, the selection tool, and drag the object or text
~ to where you want it. You do not need to select an object before you move it. Do *not*
~ a handle—dragging a handle resizes an object. You can move all objects in a
~tion at the same time in this manner.

~ press Shift *after* you depress the mouse button, the object will move along the
~est 45-degree line. This is especially helpful when you want to move an object only
~ontally, only vertically, or an equal distance horizontally and vertically.

~ing with the Keyboard

~ove selected object(s) ...	Windows	Macintosh
~kel	arrow keys	arrow keys
~xels	Shift+arrow	shift+arrow
~ixels	Ctrl+arrow	⌘+arrow
~ixels	Shift+Ctrl+arrow	shift+⌘+arrow
~selected text string	Enter	return
~line break to text	Ctrl+Enter	⌘+return

~pping—Disappearing Objects

~n you drag data display objects (such as symbols, connect lines, areas, projection
~ and so on) out of the data region and you have clipping turned on, the data display
~ts disappear, or are clipped. You can restore objects that disappear in this manner
~oosing **Edit ➤ Undo** before you do anything else. Refer to the *MINITAB Reference*
~al for more information.

~plicating Objects

You can duplicate items in a selection by choosing **Editor ➤ Duplicate**.

Centers of duplicated items are placed 20 pixels down and 20 pixels to the right of
the current selection.

You can duplicate all objects in a selection at once.

When you duplicate data display objects, the duplicated objects retain data display
editing restrictions, such as clipping attributes, and alignment restrictions.

~ng to Front / Send to Back

~an see the effect of the commands on a selected object from the following
~ations:

Before	After choosing Editor ➤ Send to Back

~ere is so[me text]

Here is some text.

~ first picture, the rectangle obscures the text string. In the second, the text is in front
~ rectangle. Choosing **Editor ➤ Bring to Front** restores the polygon to the way it
~at left.

~n you click overlapping objects, the one in front is selected. If you cannot select
~thing because an object is in front, select the object in front and send it to the back,
~select the first object.

~feature works with all objects you draw, but not between most objects generated with
~raph. You can also bring to front or send to back annotation items generated with the
~ut dialog box (that is, direct subcommands of LAYOUT).

Resizing Objects and Text

Resizing Symbols	To resize symbols you have already selected, click ⊞ the marker size button on the Attribute palette, and choose a new size from the menu.
Resizing Squares or Circles	1. Click ▲, the selection tool, if it is not already the tool in use. 2. Click and hold one of the vertex (corner) handles. 3. While holding down Shift, drag the handle until the object reaches the size you desire. 4. If you do not hold down Shift, the square or circle turns into a rectangle or ellipse. In this case, you can turn the rectangle or ellipse back into a square or circle by holding down Shift and dragging a vertex (corner) handle.
Reshaping Rectangles or Ellipses	You can do this in two ways: ■ dragging a handle at a midpoint. This adjusts either the width or the height of the object, but not both at once. ■ dragging a vertex (corner) handle. This allows you to adjust both the width and the height of the object at the same time.
Reshaping Polygons, Polylines, and Lines	You can reshape (move a vertex of) a selected polygon, polyline, or line using ▲, the selection tool. To reshape, select the polygon, then grab a handle. Drag the handle to the point where you want the vertex.
Resizing Text	You can enlarge the text itself using ⊤, the text size tool. When you enlarge or shrink the text, the width of the text area stays constant. When the resized text needs more room, the text area grows down, not across, and more lines are added to accommodate the larger text size.
Reshaping a Text Area	You can resize a selected text area using ▲, the selection tool, by grabbing a handle and dragging the handle to where you want the text area to end. When you resize text areas, you really only resize the width of the text area. The text fills as many lines as necessary in the given width.
Editing Text Strings	To edit an existing text string, double-click on it using ▲, the selection tool, edit the text in the dialog box and click **OK**. You can also select the text and press Enter to get to the text editing dialog box. You can add line breaks in a text string by pressing Ctrl+Enter (Microsoft Windows) or ⌘+return (Macintosh)

Exporting Graphs to Other Applications

Copy and Paste

With the Graph window active, choose **Edit ➤ Copy Graph**, go to the other application,
and paste.

Save as a Plotter File ⑩ (Microsoft Windows Only)

1. In the Printers dialog box of the Microsoft Windows Control Panel, add a Hewlett
   Packard Graphics Language (HPGL) Plotter to your list of available printers. Use the
   Connect button to set the plotter to print to a file. See your Microsoft Windows
   documentation for instructions.

2. In Minitab, choose **File ➤ Print Setup**, and select the HPGL Plotter.

3. With the Graph window active, choose **File ➤ Print Window**. At the prompt, type a file
   name, ending with the extension PLT.

4. Open (or import) the PLT file in another application.

Graph Editing—Double-Click a Graph to Start ⑩—all Graph Editing features

To enter edit mode, double-click on a Graph window or, from an active Graph window, choose **Editor ➤ Edit**.
If the Tool or Attribute palettes do not display, choose **Editor ➤ Show Tool Palette** and **Editor ➤ Show Attribute Palette**.

Tool Palette

Click here (once) to **hide** the Tool palette.

Click and drag here to **move** the Tool palette.

The selection tool. To select a graph object, click this button, then click the object on the graph.

The rectangle/square tool. To draw rectangles, click this button, and drag from start corner to end corner. For squares, hold Shift down, then drag from start corner to end corner.

The line tool. To draw lines, click this button, then drag from start point to end point.

The polyline tool. To draw a series of connected lines (a polyline), click here, then click to end each line segment. Select another tool or press Enter to end the line.

The text tool. To add text, click this button, drag to outline an area for the text, then type the text in the dialog box, and click **OK**.

The ellipse/circle tool. To draw ellipses, click this button, and drag from start corner to end corner. For circles, hold Shift down, then drag from start corner to end corner.

The marker tool. To draw markers/symbols, click here, then click where you want the marker.

The polygon tool. To draw fillable polygons, click here, then click at each vertex point. To end the polygon, you can click the first vertex point, press Enter, or select another tool. If you press Enter or select another tool, the last line is drawn automatically.

Attribute Palette

Click here (once) to **hide** the Attribute palette.

Click and drag here to **move** the Attribute palette.

Text Attributes change the typeface, color, and size of selected text elements.

Line Attributes change the line type, color, size, and arrowhead direction/style of selected line(s) or edge(s), or the color of foreground fill patterns.

Fill Attributes change the foreground fill pattern and background color of selected objects.

Marker and Symbol Attributes change the marker/symbol type, color, and size of selected markers/symbols.

Keyboard Shortcuts

	Windows	Macintosh
Help	F1	help
Files		
New worksheet	Ctrl+N	⌘+N
Open worksheet	Ctrl+O	⌘+O
Save worksheet	Ctrl+S	⌘+S
Print window	Ctrl+P	⌘+P
Session Window		
Submit command (default)	Enter	return
Add line break (default)	Ctrl+Enter	⌘+return
Data Window		
Next row/column	Ctrl+Enter	⌘+return
Go to ...	Ctrl+G	⌘+G
1 screen down, up, left, or right	Ctrl+arrow key	⌘+arrow key
Beginning of worksheet	Ctrl+Home	⌘+home
End of worksheet	Ctrl+End	⌘+end
Format column	Ctrl+Y	⌘+Y
Compress display	Ctrl+K	⌘+K
Enter cell edit mode	Alt+Enter	option+return
Move within active cell	Alt+arrow key	option+arrow key
Editing		
Copy (cells or text)	Ctrl+C	⌘+C
Cut (cells or text)	Ctrl+X	⌘+X
Paste/Insert (cells or text)	Ctrl+V	⌘+V
Select All (graphs, cells, or text)	Ctrl+A	⌘+A
Select an area (cells or text)	Shift+arrow	shift+arrow

	Windows	Macintosh
Dialog Boxes		
Edit last command dialog box	Ctrl+E	⌘+E
Reset defaults	F3	⌘+R
Choose Cancel	Esc	Esc
Minitab Windows		
Command Line Editor	Ctrl+L	⌘+L
Session	Ctrl+M	⌘+M
Data	Ctrl+D	⌘+D
History	Ctrl+H	⌘+H
Info	Ctrl+I	⌘+I
Switch between windows	Ctrl+Tab	⌘+L
Graphics		
To move selected object(s) ...		
1 pixel	arrow keys	arrow keys
5 pixels	Shift+arrow	shift+arrow
10 pixels	Ctrl+arrow	⌘+arrow
50 pixels	Shift+Ctrl+arrow	shift+⌘+arrow
Edit selected text string	Enter	return
Add line break to text	Ctrl+Enter	⌘+return
Canceling Operations		
Cancel a %macro, Exec, or graph	Ctrl+Break	⌘+.

tation

is Quick Reference, commands are left justified, subcommands are indented.

denotes a constant such as 8.3 or K14
denotes a column such as C12 or 'Height'
denotes either a constant or column, and sometimes a matrix
denotes a matrix such as M5
denotes an optional argument
C means you can list one or more columns

les for Typing Commands

You need only type the first four letters of any command. For %macros, type % followed by the full macro name.

Start each command and subcommand on a new line.

To use a subcommand, end the line before it with a semi-colon (;). End the last subcommand with a period.
For example: RANDOM 10 C1;
                    BINOMIAL 20 0.3.

Type the subcommand ABORT to cancel a multi-line session command.
For example: RANDOM 10 C1;
                    BINOMIAL 20 0.3;
                    ABORT.

Abbreviate lists of consecutive variables with a dash.
For example: RANDOM 10 C1-C5

Enclose file and variable names with single quotation marks.
         For example: SAVE 'SALESQ1'

Only type the commands and their arguments (**K**, **C**, **E**, or **M** as defined above). Text is for explanation only. For example, the syntax for the MEDIAN command is

MEDIAN of the values in C [put into K]

This means that you could type either:

MEDIAN C1   to display the median of C1, or
MEDIAN C1 K1   to display the median of C1 and store it in
                             the constant K1

errupting Commands

can stop the display of a command as follows:
VAX/Unix and many other mini-mainframe releases: Ctrl+C
Microsoft Windows and DOS: Ctrl+Break
Macintosh: ⌘+.

can stop typing a session command when typing subcommands by typing ABORT.

mbols

Missing Value Symbol. An * can be used as data in READ, SET, and INSERT, and in data files. Enclose the * in single quotes in commands and subcommands.

Comment Symbol. The symbol # anywhere on a line tells Minitab to ignore the rest of the line.

Continuation Symbol. To continue a command onto another line, end the first line with the symbol &.

Miscellaneous Commands

HELP	explains Minitab commands, can be Help on a command or a subcommand with its own subcommands
ABORT	cancels a multi-line command without executing it
INFO	[C…C] summarizes the worksheet (the same information can be found in the Info window)
RESTART	begin fresh Minitab session
STOP	ends the current session and exits Minitab
TYPE	'[PATH] FILENAME.EXT' display contents of a file (Windows and DOS only)
CD	[PATH] change working directory (Windows and DOS only)
DIR	[PATH] list files (Windows and DOS only)
SYSTEM	[SYSTEMCOMMAND] lets you use MS-DOS commands (Windows and DOS only)
OH	= K number of lines for height of output (not for Macintosh)
OW	= K number of spaces for width of output
IW	= K number of spaces for width of input
BRIEF	= K controls amount of output from ARIMA, BBDESIGN, CCDESIGN, CLUOBS, CLUVARS, DISCRIMINANT, FACTOR, FFDESIGN, GLM, KMEANS, MIXREG, REGRESS, RLINE, RSREG, SCDESIGN, and SLDESIGN. BRIEF 2 is the default; BRIEF 0 suppresses all output for all commands.
TSHARE	operate interactively
BATCH	operate in batch mode

Files, Data, and Output Commands

NAME	for E is 'name' … for E is 'name'	
RETRIEVE	the Minitab saved worksheet [in 'filename']	
PORTABLE	retrieve a Minitab portable worksheet	
LOTUS	retrieve a Lotus file (Windows and DOS only)	
GVIEW	open a Minitab graph (MGF) file	**❾***E*
GPAUSE	[K] controls pausing of graph windows	**❾***E*
GSAVE	[in 'file'] save a high-resolution graph or graphs	**❾***E*
REPLACE	replace existing file	
NOREPLACE	do not replace existing file	
SAVE	[in 'filename'] a copy of the worksheet	
PORTABLE	save a Minitab portable worksheet	
REPLACE	replace existing file	**❾**
NOREPLACE	do not replace existing file	**❾**
LOTUS	save in Lotus format (Windows and DOS only)	
READ	data into C…C	
With READ; FILE only:		
TAB	columns are separated with tabs	
NONAMES	columns are not named	
ALPHA	columns are in K…K	
SET	data into C	
INSERT	data [between rows K and K] of C…C	
READ, SET, and INSERT have the subcommands:		
FILE	'filename'	
FORMAT	(format statement)	
NOBS	= K	
SKIP	K lines	**❾**
END	of data	
PRINT	the data in E…E	
FORMAT	(format statement)	

WRITE	[to 'filename'] the data in C…C
FORMAT	(format statement)
TAB	separate columns with tabs
NONAMES	omit column names
REPLACE	replace existing file
NOREPLACE	do not replace existing file
OUTFILE	'filename' put all input and output in file
OW	= K output width of file
OH	= K output height of file (not for Macintosh)
NOTERM	no output to terminal
NOECHO	display no commands in outfile
NOOUTFILE	output to terminal only; ends OUTFILE
NEWPAGE	start next output on a new page
JOURNAL	['filename'] record Minitab commands in this file
NOJOURNAL	cancels JOURNAL

Editing and Manipulating Data

LET	C(K) = K (changes the number in row K of C)
DELETE	rows K…K of C…C
ERASE	all data in E…E
INSERT	data [between rows K and K] of C…C
FILE	'filename'
FORMAT	(format statement)
NOBS	= K
SKIP	K lines
COPY	C…C into C…C
COPY	C into K…K
USE	rows K…K
USE	rows where C = K…K
OMIT	rows K…K
OMIT	rows where C = K…K
COPY	K…K into K…K
COPY	K…K into C
CODE	(K…K) to K… (K…K) to K for C…C, put in C…C
ATON	input column in C, output column in C
NTOA	input column in C, output column in C
WIDTH	K characters
MAXWIDTH	K characters
SIGNIFICANT	K digits
DECIMALS	K decimal places
MISSING	(value converted to) 'text'
STACK	(E…E)… on (E…E), put in (C…C)
SUBSCRIPTS	into C
UNSTACK	(C…C) into (E…E)… (E…E)
SUBSCRIPTS	are in C
CONVERT	using table in C C, the data in C, and put in C
CONCATENATE	C…C put in C
SORT	C [carry along C…C] put into C [and C…C]
BY	C…C
DESCENDING	C…C
RANK	the values in C, put ranks into C

Arithmetic

LET E = expression
Expressions may use
- Arithmetic operators +   –   *   /   ** (exponentiation)
- Comparison operators =   ~= or <>   >   <   <=   >=
- Logical operators & | ~
and any of the following functions and column operations:

ABSOLUTE	SQRT	LOGTEN	LOGE	EXPONENTIA
ANTILOG	ROUND	SIN	COS	TAN
ASIN	ACOS	ATAN	SIGNS	NSCORES
PARSUMS	PARPRODUCTS	COUNT	N	NMISS
SUM	MEAN	STDEV	MEDIAN	MINIMUM
MAXIMUM	SSQ	SORT	RANK	LAG
EQ	NE	LT	GT	LE
GE	AND	OR	NOT	

Examples: LET C2 = SQRT(C1 - MIN(C1))
LET C3(5) = 4.5

Simple Arithmetic Operations

ADD	E to E, …, to E,	put into E
SUBTRACT	E from E	put into E
MULTIPLY	E by E , …, by E	put into E
DIVIDE	E by E	put into E
RAISE	E to the power E	put into E

Columnwise Functions

ABSOLUTE	value of E	put into E
SQRT	of E	put into E
LOGE	of E	put into E
LOGTEN	of E	put into E
EXPONENTIATE	E	put into E
ANTILOG	of E	put into E
ROUND	to integer E	put into E
SIN	of E	put into E
COS	of E	put into E
TAN	of E	put into E
ASIN	of E	put into E
ACOS	of E	put into E
ATAN	of E	put into E
SIGNS	of E	[put into E]
PARSUMS	of C	put into C
PARPRODUCTS	of C	put into C

Normal Scores

| NSCORES | of C | put into C |

Columnwise Statistics

COUNT	the number of values in	C [put into K]
N	(number of nonmissing values) in	C [put into K]
NMISS	(number of missing values) in	C [put into K]
SUM	of the values in	C [put into K]
MEAN	of the values in	C [put into K]
STDEV	of the values in	C [put into K]
MEDIAN	of the values in	C [put into K]
MINIMUM	of the values in	C [put into K]
MAXIMUM	of the values in	C [put into K]
RANGE	of the values in	C [put into K]
SSQ	(uncorrected sum of sq.) for	C [put into K]

Rowwise Statistics

RCOUNT	of E…E	put into C
RN	of E…E	put into C
RNMISS	of E…E	put into C
RSUM	of E…E	put into C
RMEAN	of E…E	put into C
RSTDEV	of E…E	put into C
RMEDIAN	of E…E	put into C
RMINIMUM	of E…E	put into C
RMAXIMUM	of E…E	put into C
RRANGE	of E…E	put into C
RSSQ	of E…E	put into C

Indicator Variables

| INDICATOR | variables for subscripts in C, | put into C…C |

sic Statistics

CRIBE	C...C
BY	C
SCRIBE	C ⑩
BY	C
CONFIDENCE	K
TITLE	for graph is 'text'
GSAVE	save graph in 'filename'

S	[C...C] ⑩

Control of the grouping:

BY	C...C
NOEMPTY	
MISSINGS	

Storage of group information:

GLABELS	C...C
GVALUES	C...C
GIDS	C...C

Storage of statistics:

MEAN	C...C
SEMEAN	C...C
STDEVIATIONS	C...C
VARIANCE	C...C
QONE	C...C
MEDIAN	C...C
QTHREE	C...C
IQRANGE	C...C
SUMS	C...C
MINIMUMS	C...C
MAXIMUMS	C...C
RANGE	C...C
N	C...C
NMISSING	C...C
COUNT	C...C
CUMN	C...C
PERCENT	C...C
CUMPERCENT	C...C
SSQ	C...C
SKEWNESS	C...C
KURTOSIS	C...C
MSSD	C...C

ERVAL	[K% confidence] assuming σ = K for C...C
ST	[of μ = K] assuming σ = K for C...C
ALTERNATIVE	= K

ERVAL	[K% confidence] for data in C...C
ST	[of μ = K] on data in C...C
ALTERNATIVE	= K

SAMPLE	test and c.i. [K% confidence] samples in C C
ALTERNATIVE	= K
POOLED	procedure
T	test and c.i. [K% confidence] data in C, groups in C
ALTERNATIVE	= K
POOLED	procedure

RELATION	between C...C [put into M]
ARIANCE	between C...C [put into M]

TER	the data in C...C put into C...C
LOCATION	[subtracting K...K]
SCALE	[dividing by K...K]
MINMAX	[with K as min and K as max]

RTEST	response in C factors in C...C ⑩
CONFIDENCE	level is K
STDEVS	store in C
VARIANCES	store in C
UPPER	store in C
LOWER	store in C
NOTABLE	suppress table of st.dev. and conf. limits
TITLE	for graph is 'text'
GSAVE	save graph in 'filename'

Regression

REGRESS	C on K predictors C...C
NOCONSTANT	do not fit y-intercept
CONSTANT	fit y-intercept (default)
WEIGHTS	are in C
SRESIDUALS	put into C
FITS	put into C
MSE	put into K
COEFFICIENTS	put into C
XPXINV	put into M
RMATRIX	put into M
HI	put into C (leverage)
RESIDUALS	put into C (observed - fit)
TRESIDUALS	put into C (deleted Studentized)
COOKD	put into C (Cook's distance)
DFITS	put into C
PREDICT	for E...E
CONFIDENCE	level is K
PFITS	put fits into C
PSDFITS	put std. dev. of fits into C
CLIMITS	put conf. limits into C C
PLIMITS	put pred. limits into C C
VIF	(variance inflation factor)
DW	(Durbin-Watson statistic)
PURE	(pure error lack-of-fit test)
XLOF	(experimental lack-of-fit test)
TOLERANCE	K [K]

STEPWISE	regress C on predictors C...C
NOCONSTANT	do not fit y-intercept
CONSTANT	fit y-intercept (default)
FENTER	= K (default is 4)
FREMOVE	= K (default is 4)
FORCE	C...C
ENTER	C...C
REMOVE	C...C
BEST	K alternative predictors
STEPS	= K (default depends on output width)

BREG	C on predictors C...C
NOCONSTANT	do not fit y-intercept
CONSTANT	fit y-intercept (default)
INCLUDE	predictors C...C in all models
BEST	K models
NVARS	K [up to K]
NOWARN	suppress warning for model with many predictors

%FITLINE	regress C on the predictor in C ⑨E
CONFIDENCE	level is K
FITS	put fits into C
RESIDUALS	put residuals into C
CI	display confidence bands
PI	display prediction bands
TITLE	for graph is 'text'
GSAVE	save graph in 'filename'

%RESPLOTS	residuals in C, fits in C ⑩
TITLE	for graph is 'text'
GSAVE	save graph in 'filename'

NOCONSTANT	do not fit y-intercept in REGRESS, STEPWISE, and BREG commands that follow
CONSTANT	fit y-intercept in REGRESS, STEPWISE, and BREG commands that follow
BRIEF	output code K

Analysis of Variance

AOVONEWAY	aov on samples in C…C	
ONEWAY	aov on data in C, levels in C [put residuals in C [fits in C]]	
TUKEY	[family error rate K]	
FISHER	[individual error rate K]	
DUNNETT	[family error rate K] for control group K	
MCB	[family error rate K] best is K	
TWOWAY	aov on data in C, levels in C C [put residuals in C [fits in C]]	
ADDITIVE	model	
MEANS	for the factors C [C]	

%ANOM	analysis of means on data in C, levels in C [C]	**9** *E*
TABLE	display table of statistics	
%BANOM	analysis of means on binomial data in C, sample size K	**9** *E*
TABLE	display table of statistics	
%PANOM	analysis of means on Poisson data in C	**9** *E*

%ANOM, %BANOM, and %PANOM have the subcommands:

ALPHA	level is K
TITLE	for graph is 'text'
GSAVE	save graph in 'filename'

ANOVA	model
RANDOM	C…C
EMS	print table of expected mean squares, estimated variance components, and error term in each F-test
FITS	put into C…C
RESIDUALS	put into C…C
MEANS	for termlist
TEST	for termlist / errorterm
RESTRICT	use restricted model
MANOVA	[termlist [/ errorterm]]
SSCP	print hypothesis matrix and error matrix
EIGEN	print table of eigenvalues and eigenvectors
PARTIAL	print matrix of partial correlations
NOUNIVARIATE	suppress univariate output
ANCOVA	model
COVARIATES	are in C…C
FITS	put into C…C
RESIDUALS	put into C…C
MEANS	for termlist
TEST	for termlist / errorterm
GLM	model
COVARIATES	are in C…C
WEIGHTS	are in C
FITS	put into C…C
RESIDUALS	put into C…C
SRESIDUALS	put into C…C
TRESIDUALS	put into C…C
HI	put into C
COOKD	put into C…C
DFITS	put into C…C
XMATRIX	put into M
COEFFICIENTS	put into C…C
MEANS	for termlist
TEST	for termlist / errorterm
MANOVA	[termlist [/ errorterm]]
SSCP	print hypothesis matrix and error matrix
EIGEN	print table of eigenvalues and eigenvectors
PARTIAL	print matrix of partial correlations
NOUNIVARIATE	suppress univariate output
BRIEF	output code K
TOLERANCE	K [K]

%MAIN	main effects plots for factors in C…C	**10**
%INTERACT	interaction plots for factors in C…C	**10**
FULL	display full matrix of plots	
NOCENTER	remove center points from factor level columns	

%MAIN and %INTERACT have the following subcommands:

RESPONSE	data in C
LSMEANS	data in C
YMIN	y-axis minimum is K
YMAX	y-axis maximum is K
TITLE	for graph is 'text'
GSAVE	save graph in 'filename'

Multivariate Analysis

DISCRIMINANT	groups in C, predictors in C…C
QUADRATIC	discrimination
PRIORS	are in K…K
LDF	coefficients put in C…C
FITS	put in C [XVAL fits in C]
XVAL	use cross-validation
PREDICT	for E…E
BRIEF	output code K
PCA	principal component analysis of C…C
COVARIANCE	matrix
NCOMP	number of components is K
COEFFICIENTS	put into C…C
SCORES	put into C…C
FACTOR	[C…C]
CORRELATION	factor the correlation matrix [M]
COVARIANCE	factor the covariance matrix [M]
NFACTORS	extract K factors
ML	use maximum likelihood (default is PCA)
PRIORS	use C as initial communality estimates in ML
MAXITERATIONS	K maximum number of iterations for ML
CONVERGENCE	K criterion for convergence in ML
INLOADINGS	input C…C as loadings
SORT	sort loadings, [print all loadings less than K as 0.0]
VMAX	use varimax rotation
QMAX	use quartimax rotation
EMAX	use equamax rotation
OMAX	use orthomax rotation with $\gamma = K$
EIGEN	store eigenvalues in C, vectors in M
LOADINGS	store loadings in C…C
COEFFICIENTS	store factor score coefficients in C…C
SCORES	store factor scores in C…C
RESIDUAL	store residual matrix in M
ROTMAT	store rotation matrix in M
BRIEF	output code K

CLUOBS	cluster observations in C…C or M
EUCLIDEAN	use Euclidean distance (default)
SQEUCLIDEAN	use squared Euclidean distance
PEARSON	use Pearson distance
SQPEARSON	use squared Pearson distance
MANHATTAN	use Manhattan distance
STANDARDIZE	standardize variables before clustering
MEMBER	save cluster membership in C
DISTANCE	save the distance between obs. and centroids in C..
CLUVARS	cluster variables in C…C or M
CORRELATION	use correlation distance (default)
ABSCORRELATION	use absolute correlation distance

CLUOBS and CLUVARS have the following subcommands:

SINGLE	use single linkage (default)
AVERAGE	use average linkage
COMPLETE	use complete linkage
MCQUITTY	use McQuitty linkage
CENTROID	use centroid linkage
MEDIAN	use median linkage
WARD	use Ward linkage
NUMBER	cut dendrogram to obtain K clusters
CUT	cut dendrogram at K similarity level
DENDROGRAM	display dendrogram
TYPE	line type for each cluster is K…K
COLOR	line color for each cluster is K…K
SIZE	line size for each cluster is K…K
TITLE	for dendrogram is 'text'
GSAVE	save dendrogram in 'filename'
YDISTANCE	use distance on the y-axis, default is simila
MULTIPAGE	display each cluster in a separate window
DMATRIX	save the distance matrix in M
BRIEF	output code K
KMEANS	cluster observations in C…C
STANDARDIZE	standardize variables before clustering
NUMBER	extract K clusters
INITIAL	use the initial partition in C
MEMBERSHIP	save cluster membership in C
DISTANCE	save the distance between obs. and centroids in C..
BRIEF	output code K

nparametrics

	test [above and below K] for C...C
T	sign test [median = K] for C...C
ALTERNATIVE	= K
ERVAL	sign c.i. [K% confidence] for C...C
ST	Wilcoxon one-sample rank test [median = K] for C...C
ALTERNATIVE	= K
ERVAL	Wilcoxon c.i. [K% confidence] for C...C
I-WHITNEY	two-sample rank test and c.i. [K% confidence] on C C
ALTERNATIVE	= K
KAL-WALLIS	test for data in C, subscripts in C
O	median test, data in C, subscripts in C [put res. in C [fits in C]]
CELL	statistics store in C, C, C, C, C [C, C]
MAN	data in C, treatment in C, blocks in C [put res. in C [fits in C]]
H	averages for C, put into C [indices into C C]
F	for C and C, put into C [indices into C C]
PE	y in C, x in C, put slopes into C [indices into C C]

les

	the data in C...C
COUNTS	
PERCENTS	
CUMCOUNTS	cumulative counts
CUMPERCENTS	cumulative percents
ALL	all four statistics above
STORE	C...C ⑩
QUARE	test on table stored in C...C
	the data classified by C...C
MEANS	for C...C
MEDIANS	for C...C
SUMS	for C...C
MINIMUMS	for C...C
MAXIMUMS	for C...C
STDEV	for C...C
STATS	for C...C
DATA	for C...C
N	for C...C
NMISS	for C...C
PROPORTION	of cases = K [through K] for C...C
COUNTS	
ROWPERCENTS	
COLPERCENTS	
TOTPERCENTS	
CHISQUARE	analysis [output code = K]
MISSING	level for classification variable C...C
NOALL	in margins
ALL	for C...C
FREQUENCIES	are in C
LAYOUT	K rows by K columns

e Series

END	analysis for the data in C	⑩
QUADRATIC	use quadratic trend model	
GROWTH	use exponential growth trend model	
SCURVE	use Pearl-Reed logistic trend model	
PRIORS	use coefficients K K [K]	
WEIGHTS	to compute smoothed coefficients are K K [K]	
more shared subcommands at right		
COMP	analysis for the data in C with seasonal length K	⑩
MULTIPLICATIVE	model (default)	
ADDITIVE	model	
NOTREND	do not include a trend component	
START	initial seasonal period is K	
TREND	store the trend component values in C	
DETREND	store the detrended data in C	
SEASONAL	store the seasonal component values in C	
DESEASONAL	store the deseasonalized data in C	
more shared subcommands at right		

%MA	for the data in C, with a moving average of length K	⑩
CENTER	the moving averages	
AVERAGES	store the moving averages in C	
UPPER	store the upper prediction limits in C	
LOWER	store the lower prediction limits in C	
SMPLOT	plot smoothed values vs. actual data	
more shared subcommands below		
%SES	single exponential smoothing for the data in C	⑩
WEIGHT	to use to smooth the data is K	
INITIAL	smooth value is average of first K values	
SMOOTHED	store the smoothed data in C	
UPPER	store the upper prediction limits in C	
LOWER	store the lower prediction limits in C	
SMPLOT	plot smoothed values vs. actual data	
more shared subcommands below		
%DES	double exponential smoothing for the data in C	⑩
WEIGHTS	for level component are K, for trend component are K	
SMOOTHED	store the smoothed data in C	
LEVEL	store the level component values in C	
TREND	store the trend component values in C	
UPPER	store the upper prediction limits in C	
LOWER	store the lower prediction limits in C	
SMPLOT	plot smoothed values vs. actual data	
more shared subcommands below		
%WINTMULT	seasonal exponential smoothing for the data in C with seasonal length K	⑩
more shared subcommands below		
%WINTADD	seasonal exponential smoothing for the data in C with seasonal length K	⑩
more shared subcommands below		

%WINTMULT and %WINTADD have the subcommands:

WEIGHTS	for level component K, for trend component K, for seasonal component K
SMOOTHED	store the smoothed data in C
LEVEL	store the level component values in C
TREND	store the trend component values in C
SEASONAL	store the seasonal component values in C
UPPER	store the upper prediction limits in C
LOWER	store the lower prediction limits in C
SMPLOT	plot smoothed values vs. actual data

%TREND, %DECOMP, %MA, %SES, %DES, %WINTMULT, and %WINTADD have the subcommands:

FORECASTS	generate K forecasts
ORIGIN	begin forecasts at time K
RESIDUALS	store the residuals in C
FITS	store the fits in C
FSTORE	store the forecasts in C
NOPLOT	suppress the plot
TABLE	display additional output
TITLE	for graph is 'text'
GSAVE	save graph in 'filename'

DIFFERENCES	[of lag K] for data in C, put into C
LAG	[by K] for data in C, put into C
ACF	[with up to K lags] for series in C [put into C]
PACF	[with up to K lags] for series in C [put into C]

%ACF	for series in C	⑩
LBQ	store Ljung-Box Q statistics in C	
%PACF	for series in C	⑩

%ACF and %PACF have the subcommands:

MAXLAG	number of lags is K
CORR	store (partial for %PACF) autocorrelations in C
TSTATS	store t-statistics in C
TITLE	for graph is 'text'
GSAVE	save graph in 'filename'

CCF	[with up to K lags] between series in C and C
ARIMA	p = K, d = K, q = K, P = K, D = K, Q = K, S = K, data in C
	[put residuals in C [predicted values in C [parameters in C]]]
NOCONSTANT	do not fit y-intercept
CONSTANT	fit y-intercept (default)
STARTING	values are in C
FORECAST	[origin = K] up to K leads [forecasts in C [limits in C C]]
BRIEF	output code K

Exploratory Data Analysis

LVALS	of C [put letter values in C [mids in C [spreads in C]]]
MPOLISH	C, levels in C C [put residuals in C [fits in C]]
COLUMNS	start iteration with column medians
ITERATIONS	= K
EFFECTS	put common into K, rows into C, columns into C
COMPARISONS	values, put into C
RLINE	y in C, x in C [put residuals in C [fits in C [coefficients in C]]]
MAXITERATIONS	= K max. number of iterations
RSMOOTH	C, put rough into C, smooth into C
SMOOTH	by 3RSSH, twice
CPLOT	condensed plot of C vs. C
LINES	= K
CHARACTERS	= K
XBOUNDS	= from K to K
YBOUNDS	= from K to K
CTABLE	coded table data in C, row levels in C, column levels in C
MAXIMUM	value in each cell should be coded
MINIMUM	value in each cell should be coded
ROOTOGRAM	[data in C [use bin boundaries in C]]
BOUNDARIES	put in C
DRRS	put in C
FITTED	values, put in C
COUNTS	put in C
FREQUENCIES	are in C [bin boundaries are in C]
MEAN	= K
STDEV	= K

Distributions and Random Data

RANDOM	K observations into C...C
BERNOULLI	trials p = K
PDF	for values in E...E [put results in E...E]
CDF	for values in E...E [put results in E...E]
INVCDF	for values in E...E [put results in E...E]

RANDOM, PDF, CDF, and INVCDF have the subcommands:

BINOMIAL	n = K, p = K
POISSON	μ = K
INTEGER	discrete uniform on integers K to K
DISCRETE	values in C and probabilities in C
NORMAL	[μ = K [σ = K]]
UNIFORM	[continuous on the interval K to K]
T	degrees of freedom = K
F	df numerator = K, df denominator = K
CAUCHY	[a = K [b = K]]
LAPLACE	[a = K [b = K]]
LOGISTIC	[a = K [b = K]]
LOGNORMAL	[μ = K [σ = K]]
CHISQUARE	df = K
EXPONENTIAL	[mean = K]
GAMMA	a = K b = K
WEIBULL	a = K b = K
BETA	a = K b = K

SAMPLE	K rows from C...C put into C...C
REPLACE	sample with replacement
BASE	for random number generator = K

Matrices

READ	[from 'filename'] into a K by K matrix M
PRINT	M...M
TRANSPOSE	M into M
INVERT	M into M
DEFINE	K into K by K matrix M
DIAGONAL	is C, form into M
DIAGONAL	of M, put into C
COPY	C...C into M
COPY	M into C...C
COPY	M into M
USE	rows K...K
OMIT	rows K...K
ERASE	M...M
EIGEN	for M put values into C [vectors into M]

In the following commands E can be either C, K, or M:

ADD	E to E,	put into E
SUBTRACT	E from E,	put into E
MULTIPLY	E by E,	put into E

Subcommands		XBARCHART C E	RCHART C E	SCHART C E	%XRCHART C E	%XSCHART C E	ICHART C	MRCHART C	%IMRCHART C	EWMACHART C E	MACHART C E	%CUSUM C K	%ZONE C E [10] X	%ZMRCHART C C [10] X	PCHART C E	NPCHART C E	CCHART C	UCHART C E
		Variables Control Charts													**Attributes Control Charts**			
…ATE	K…K	●	●	●			●	●		●	●				●	●	●	●
	K														●	●		
	K	●			●	●			●	●	●		●				●	●
	K	●	●	●	●	●	●	●	●	●	●	●	●					
			●	●	●					●	●	●	●					
…|	K	●	●	●			●	●	●	●	●	●	●					
…ROUP	K	●	●	●	●	●				●	●				●	●	●	●
	K										●							
…T	K									●								
	K…K	●					●								●	●	●	●
…S	K…K														●	●	●	●
…PE	K	●	●	●			●	●		●	●				●	●	●	●
…OLOR	K																	
…ZE	K																	
	C																	
…ABEL	['text' of C]																	
…ONT	K	●	●	●			●	●		●	●				●	●	●	●
…OLOR	K																	
…ZE	K																	
	C (no subcommands)[a]				●	●			●					●				
…ER	C													●				
…S	C													●				
…RATE	(default)													●				
…ED														●				
…-														●				
														●				
…AY	K												●	●				
…ET	K											●						
	K											●						
	K K											●						
…K	K											●						
…r												●						
…TS	K K K K												●					
…ES	C												●					

cs Subcommands for Control Chart ands:

a Display (p. 20):
MBOL and CONNECT only

notation (p. 20): All

me Customization (p. 21):
except TRANSPOSE and MARGIN   ● … ● ●   ● ●   ● ●   ● ● ● ●

gions (p. 21):
except LEGEND/NOLEGEND,
ERLAY/NOOVERLAY, and SAME

, Input, and Output (p. 21): All

cs Options for %graphs:

a   for graph is 'text'
E[a]   save graph in 'filename'   ● ●   ●   ● ● ●

With %graphs you may include up to one TITLE subcommand, one GSAVE subcommand, and one STAMP subcommand. TITLE, GSAVE, and STAMP do not have subcommands.

Quality Planning Tools ⑨E (unless noted)

%RUNCHART	C E	⑩X
MEANS	(default)	
MEDIANS		
TITLE	for graph is 'text'	
GSAVE	save the graph in 'filename'	
%PARETO	C	
OTHERS	K	
COUNTS	C	
BY	C	⑩
SEPARATE		⑩
INDEPEND		⑩
TITLE	for graph is 'text'	
GSAVE	save the graph in 'filename'	
%FISHBONE		⑩
BR1	C	
BR2	C	
BR3	C	
BR4	C	
BR5	C	
BR6	C	
NOEMPTY		
NAM1	'text'	
NAM2	'text'	
NAM3	'text'	
NAM4	'text'	
NAM5	'text'	
NAM6	'text'	
NOLABELS		
EFFECT	'text'	
TITLE	for graph is 'text'	
GSAVE	save the graph in 'filename'	

(In Release ⑨, the %FISHBONE subcommands BR1-BR6 were named MEN, MACHINES,MATERIALS,METHODS, MEASURES, ENVIRON, respectively, each with a column argument, and NAM1-NAM6 didn't exist— VAX 9 Enhanced only)

Process Capability ⑨E (unless noted)

%CAPA	C E		
TARGET	K		
%SIXPACK	C E		
BREAKOUT	K		⑩
TEST			⑩

%CAPA and %SIXPACK have the subcommands:

USPEC	K
LSPEC	K
MU	K
SIGMA	K
RBAR	
RSPAN	K
TOTAL	
TOLER	K
TITLE	'text'
GSAVE	'filename'

USPEC and LSPEC are the specification limits. You must use at least one of these.

Character (and G-Style Hi-Res) Control Charts

These are character (typewriter-style, or standard) graphics commands. For Release 9 (Enhanced) and above — from the Session window type the command GSTD to enable character graphs. To re-enable high-resolution (professional) graphics commands, type GPRO. These charts are available as high-resolution graphics commands with the same names and with many more options. For older releases with G commands, place a G in front of the command name to get a high-resolution plot.

GSTD	enable character (standard) graphics
GPRO	enable high-resolution (professional) graphics
XBARCHART	for C...C, subgroups are in E
MU	= K
SIGMA	= K
RBAR	use $\overline{R}$ to estimate σ
RSPAN	= K
TEST	K...K
SUBGROUP	size is K

more shared subcommands below

RCHART	for C...C, subgroups are in E
SIGMA	= K
RBAR	use $\overline{R}$ to estimate σ
SUBGROUP	size is K

more shared subcommands below

SCHART	for C...C, subgroups are in E
SIGMA	= K
RBAR	use $\overline{R}$ to estimate σ
SUBGROUP	size is K

more shared subcommands below

ICHART	for C...C
MU	= K
SIGMA	= K
RSPAN	= K
TEST	K...K

more shared subcommands below

MACHART	for C...C, subgroups are in E
MU	= K
SIGMA	= K
RBAR	use $\overline{R}$ to estimate σ
SPAN	= K
RSPAN	= K
SUBGROUP	size is K

more shared subcommands below

EWMACHART	for C...C, subgroups are in E
MU	= K
SIGMA	= K
RBAR	use $\overline{R}$ to estimate σ
WEIGHT	= K
RSPAN	= K
SUBGROUP	size is K

more shared subcommands below

MRCHART	for C...C
SIGMA	= K
RSPAN	= K

more shared subcommands below

PCHART	number of nonconformities are in C...C, sample size =
P	= K
TEST	K...K
SUBGROUP	size is K

more shared subcommands below

NPCHART	number of nonconformities are in C...C, sample size =
P	= K
TEST	K...K
SUBGROUP	size is K

more shared subcommands below

CCHART	number of nonconformities are in C...C
MU	= K
TEST	K...K

more shared subcommands below

UCHART	number of nonconformities are in C...C, sample size =
MU	= K
TEST	K...K
SUBGROUP	size is K

more shared subcommands below

All character control charts have the subcommands:

SLIMITS	are K...K
HLINES	at E...E
ESTIMATE	using just samples K...K
YLABEL	= 'text'
XLABEL	= 'text'
YINCREMENT	= K
YSTART	at K [end at K]
XSTART	at K [end at K]
TITLE	= 'text'
FOOTNOTE	= 'text'

ctorial Designs ⑧

SIGN	K factors [K runs]
BLOCKS	K or termlist
REPLICATES	K
CENTER	K
FRACTION	K
FOLD	[fact…fact]
ADD	fact = term … fact = term
ALIAS	K
RANDOMIZE	[using base K]
XMATRIX	C…C
LEVELS	K…K or C
TERMS	C
BRIEF	K

SIGN	K factors [K runs]
REPLICATES	K
CENTER	K
RANDOMIZE	[using base K]
XMATRIX	C…C
LEVELS	are in K…K or C
TORIAL	model
BLOCKS	C
COVARIATES	are in C…C
EFFECTS	put in C…C
COEFFICIENTS	put in C…C
FITS	put in C…C
RESIDUALS	put in C…C
SRESIDUALS	put in C…C
TRESIDUALS	put in C…C
HI	put in C
COOKD	put in C…C
DFITS	put in C…C
XMATRIX	put in M
MEANS	for termlist
CUBES	for termlist
PLOT	normal probability plot of effects
ALIAS	[information up to order K]
TOLERANCE	K [K]

M	C C C	⑨
BLOCK	C	

ture Models ⑩

SIGN	K
SIGN	K K

DESIGN and SLDESIGN have the following subcommands:

MATRIX	C…C
UGMENT	design using axial points
OTAL	K
OWER	K…K
SEUDO	design
ROPORTIONS	design
ANDOMIZE	[K]
RIEF	K

G	C…C = C…C
LOCKS	C
UADRATIC	design
PECIALCUBIC	design
ULLCUBIC	design
TS	put in C…C
ESIDUALS	put in C…C
RESIDUALS	put in C…C
RESIDUALS	put in C…C
I	put in C
OOKD	put in C…C
FITS	put in C…C
OEFFICIENTS	put in C…C
MATRIX	put in M
RIEF	K
OLERANCE	K [K]

Response Surface Designs ⑨ (unless noted)

CCDESIGN	K factors
HALF	design
ALPHA	K
BLOCKS	K
CENTER	K [K]
BBDESIGN	K factors
BLOCKS	design
CENTER	K

CCDESIGN and BBDESIGN have the subcommands:

RANDOMIZE	[using base K]
XMATRIX	put in C…C
LEVELS	K K, …, K K or C
BRIEF	K

RSREG	C…C = C…C
BLOCKS	C
SQUARES	design
INTERACTIONS	design
FULL	design
FITS	put in C…C
RESIDUALS	put in C…C
SRESIDUALS	put in C…C
TRESIDUALS	put in C…C
HI	put in C
COOKD	put in C…C
DFITS	put in C…C
COEFFICIENTS	put in C…C
XMATRIX	put in M
EIGEN	put in C M
QUADRATIC	put in C…C
BRIEF	K
TOLERANCE	K [K]

RSCONTOUR	C C	⑩
HIGH		
LOW		
MIDDLE		
HOLD	K…K	
ALLPAIRS		
SINGLE	C C	
LEVELS	K…K or C	
NLEVELS	K	
NMESH	K K	

Data Display Subcommands (SYMBOL and CONNECT only see page 20)
Annotation Subcommands (All—see page 20)
Frame Customization Subcommands (All except MARGIN—see page 21)
Regions Subcommands (All except LEGEND / NOLEGEND,
    OVERLAY / NOOVERLAY, and SAME—see page 21)
File Subcommands (All—see page 21)

RSSURFACE	see *3D Graphics* on page 19	⑩

(Note: RS Wireframe menu command is RSSURFACE with different subcommands)

%MAIN	see *Analysis of Variance* on page 12	⑩
%INTERACT	see *Analysis of Variance* on page 12	⑩
%RESPLOTS	see *Regression* on page 11	⑩

Plots, Charts, and Histograms

Command	PLOT C*C	TSPLOT C	BOXPLOT BOXPLOT	CONTOURPLOT C*C*C C⑩	MATRIXPLOT C...C ⑩ MATRIXPLOT C...C*C...C^a	CHART C CHART C*C	HISTOGRAM C
Unique Subcommands		INDEX [K...K] SECOND [K...K] MINUTE [K...K] HOUR [K...K] DAY [K...K] MONTH [K...K] QUARTER [K...K] YEAR [K...K] START K [K...K] TDISPLAY K [K [K]]	C C*C	LEVELS K...K or C NLEVELS K REGULAR [K] IRREGULAR [K] NMESH K K MESH K K...K or K C	JITTER [K K] NOJITTER LL UR FULL DIAGONAL BOUNDARY	*Functions for y-axis variable:* COUNT (C) N (C) NMISS (C) SUM (C) MEAN (C) STDEV (C) MEDIAN (C) MINIMUM (C) MAXIMUM (C) SSQ (C) CLUSTER C [K] STACK C INCREASING or DECREASING CPERCENT CUMULATIVE	FREQUENCY or PERCENT or DENSITY NINTERVAL K [K] CUMULATIVE CUTPOINT [K...K] or [C] MIDPOINT [K...K] or [C]
	JITTER [K K] NOJITTER						
Data Display Subcommands (see page 20 for sub-subcommands)	SYMBOL [C...C] CONNECT [C...C] PROJECT [C...C] AREA [C...C] LOWESS [C...C] ⑩	SYMBOL [C...C] CONNECT [C...C] PROJECT [C...C] AREA [C...C] LOWESS [C...C] ⑩	BOX [C] SYMBOL [C] CONNECT [C]	CONNECT AREA	SYMBOL [C...C] CONNECT [C...C] PROJECT [C...C] AREA [C...C] ⑩ LOWESS	SYMBOL [C...C] CONNECT [C...C] PROJECT [C...C] AREA [C...C] BAR	SYMBOL [C...C] CONNECT [C...C] PROJECT [C...C] AREA [C...C] LOWESS [C...C] BAR
Annotation Subcommands (see page 20)	ALL	ALL	ALL	ALL	ALL	ALL	ALL
Frame Customization Subcommands (see page 21)	ALL	ALL	ALL	ALL	All except MINIMUM, MAXIMUM, and TRANSPOSE	ALL	ALL
Regions Subcommands (see page 21)	ALL	ALL	ALL	ALL	All except OVERLAY/ NOOVERLAY and SAME	ALL	ALL
Multiple Graphs	PLOT C*C...C*C	TSPLOT C...C	BOXPLOT C*C...C*C BOXPLOT C...C	CONTOURPLOT C*C*C ...C*C*C	not applicable	CHART C*C...C*C CHART C...C	HISTOGRAM C...C

a. Draftsman plot menu command uses this form of MATRIXPLOT

Layouts (for Multiple Graphs in a Window, Text Charts, etc.)

LAYOUT
TITLE	'text'
FOOTNOTE	'text'
TEXT	K K 'text'
MARKER	K K,..., K K or C C
LINE	K K,..., K K or C C
POLYGON	K K,..., K K or C C
ASPECT	K K

Graphs ⑩

Command	SURFACEPLOT [a]	C*C*C	PLTX	C*C*C	RSSURFACE [b][c] C C	
que Subcommands	REGULAR				HIGH	
	IRREGULAR	[K]			LOW	
	NMESH	K K			MIDDLE	
	MESH	K K...K			HOLD	K...K
		or K C			ALLPAIRS	
	SURFACE				SINGLE	C C
	TYPE	K			NMESH	K K
	COLOR	K			SURFACE	
	ETYPE	K			TYPE	K
	ECOLOR	K			COLOR	K
	ESIZE	K			ETYPE	K
					ECOLOR	K
					ESIZE	K
Display Subcommands (page 20 for subcommands)	SYMBOL	[C...C][d]	SYMBOL	[C...C]	SYMBOL	
	PROJECT	[C...C][d]	PROJECT	[C...C]	PROJECT	
otation Subcommands (page 20 for subcommands)	TITLE	'text'	TITLE	'text'	TITLE	'text'
	FOOTNOTE	'text'	FOOTNOTE	'text'	FOOTNOTE	'text'
e Customization commands	None		None		None	
ons Subcommands (page 21 for subcommands)	None		LAYOUT		None	
			ENDLAYOUT			
			LEGEND	[K K K]		
			NOLEGEND			
			ASPECT	K K		
fects	VPOSITION	K K K	VPOSITION	K K K	VPOSITION	K K K
	VTARGET	K K K	VTARGET	K K K	VTARGET	K K K
	VUP	K K K	VUP	K K K	VUP	K K K
	VFIELD	K K	VFIELD	K K	VFIELD	K K
	VPROJECTION	K	VPROJECTION	K	VPROJECTION	K
	VASPECT	[K K K]	VASPECT	[K K K]	VASPECT	[K K K]
	VBOX	K	VBOX	K	VBOX	K
ghting and Rendering	HSREMOVAL	K	HSREMOVAL	K	HSREMOVAL	K
	LSHADING	K [K]			LSHADING	K [K]
	LIGHT	K K K			LIGHT	K K K
	COLOR	K			COLOR	K
	VISIBILITY	K			VISIBILITY	K
	LBRIGHT	K			LBRIGHT	K

3D Wireframe menu command is SURFACEPLOT with different argument settings.
RS Wireframe menu command is RSSURFACE with different argument settings.
RSCONTOUR, a related graph, is described in *Response Surface Designs* on page 17.
Grouping functionality is not on menus.

Make Mesh Data ⑩

%MESH	C K K C K K
NXMESH	K
NYMESH	K
FUNCTION	K to create z data, store in C
PARAMS	for function are K...K

raphs

RGPLOT C C ⑩		%INTPLOT C C ⑩		%NORMPLOT C ⑨		%WEIBPLOT C ⑨		%PIE C ⑩		Other %Graphs	on page
TION	K	TYPE	K	PROBS	C	PROBS	C	COUNTS	C	**Statistics:**	
RGIN	K	CONSTANT	K	SWTEST		TITLE	'text'	START	K	%DESCRIBE	11
BEL	'label'	SIDE	K	(Ryan-Joiner, sim. to				EXPLODE	K...K	%VARTEST	11
BEL	'label'	SHOWBAR		Shapiro-Wilk)				ORDER	K	%FITLINE and %RESPLOT	11
CK	K...K	POOL		KSTEST ⑩				COMBINE	K	%ANOM, %BANOM, and %PANOM	12
CK	K...K	YLABEL	'label'	(Kolmogorov-Smirnov				NOMISS		%MAIN and %INTERACT	12
N	K...K	XLABEL	'label'	goodness-of-fit)				LABEL	K	%TREND, %DECOMP, %MA, %SES,	
N	K...K	STYPE	K	TITLE	'text'			LINES		%DES, %WINTMULT, and %WINTADD	13
N	K	SCOLOR	K					TYPES	C	%ACF and %PACF	13
AX	K	SSIZE	K					COLORS	C	**Quality Control and DOE:**	
N	K	LTYPE	K					NOCOLOR		%XRCHART	15
AX	K	LCOLOR	K					TITLE	'text'	%XSCHART	15
E	K	LSIZE	K							%IMRCHART	15
LOR	K	BTYPE	K							%CUSUM	15
E	K	BETYPE	K							%ZONE	15
EL	K	BCOLOR	K							%ZMRCHART	15
IGLE	K	BECOLOR	K							%RUNCHART	16
FFSET	K	BESIZE	K							%PARETO	16
E	'text'	BBASE	K							%FISHBONE	16
		TITLE	'text'							%CAPA	16
										%SIXPACK	16
										%FORM	17

Data Display Subcommands ⑨E (unless noted)

SYMBOL [C...C][a]	CONNECT[C...C][a]	PROJECT [C...C]	AREA [C...C][a]	BAR [C...C]	BOX [C] (BOXPLOT only)	LOWESS [C...C]
FONT K...K or C						
TYPE K...K or 'char...char' or C	TYPE K...K or C	TYPE K...K or C	TYPE K...K or C	TYPE K...K or C	TYPE K...K or C	TYPE K..C
COLOR K...K or C	COLOR K...K or C	COLOR K...K or C	COLOR K...K or C	COLOR K...K or C	COLOR K...K or C	COLOR K..C
SIZE K...K or C	SIZE K...K or C	SIZE K...K or C				SIZE K..C
		DIRECTION K	DIRECTION K			
		BASE K...K or C	BASE K...K or C	BASE K...K or C		
			ETYPE K...K or C	ETYPE K...K or C	ETYPE K...K or C	
			ECOLOR K...K or C	ECOLOR K...K or C	ECOLOR K...K or C	
			ESIZE K...K or C	ESIZE K...K or C	ESIZE K...K or C	
				CHART only: WIDTH K...K or C	WIDTH K...K or C	
LABEL[b] ['label'...'label' or C]					PROPORTIONAL [K]	FITS C..
TFONT[b] K						RESIDUALS C..
TCOLOR[b] K						
TSIZE[b] K	STRAIGHT or		STRAIGHT or		CI [K] or	
ANGLE[b] K	STEP [K]		STEP [K]		RANGE or	F K
PLACEMENT[b] K K					IQRANGE (default)	NSTEPS K
OFFSET[b] K K	PLOT only: ORDER K		PLOT only: ORDER K			
BOXPLOT only: MEDIAN or OUTLIER or INDIVIDUAL					WHISKER (default) or NOWHISKER	

a. Grouping syntax [C...C] not available for Contour Plots, Response Surface Contour Plots, or Control Charts.
b. Label commands not available for 3D Graphs or Control Charts.

Annotation Subcommands ⑨E

Subcommand	TITLE 'title'	FOOTNOTE 'footnote'	TEXT K K 'text'	LINE K K...K K or C C	POLYGON K K...K K or C C	MARKER K K...K or C C
LEFT	●	● (default)				
CENTER	● (default)	●				
RIGHT	●	●				
TFONT K	●	●	●			
TCOLOR K	●	●	●			
TSIZE K	●	●	●			
ANGLE K	●	●	●			
PLACEMENT K K	●	●	●			
OFFSET K K	●	●	●			
TYPE K				●	●	●
COLOR K				●	●	●
SIZE K				●	●	●
ETYPE K					●	
ECOLOR K					●	
ESIZE K					●	

...ommand		AXIS K [K K] or C [K K]	TICK K [K...K or C] or C [K...K or C]	REFERENCE K K...K or K C or C K...K or C C	GRID K or C	FRAME (default) / NOFRAME	MARGIN K K K K	MINIMUM K K	MAXIMUM K K	TRANSPOSE ⑩
	K	•	•	•	•					
...L	['label'...'label'] or [C]a	•	•	•						
...T	K	•	•	•						
...OR	K	•	•	•						
...E	K	•	•	•						
...E	K	•	•	•						
...EMENT	K K	•	•	•						
...ET	K K	•	•	•						
	K or K [K]	•	•	•	•					
...R	K or K [K]	•	•	•	•					
	K or K [K]	•	•	•	•					
...BER	K [K]		•							
...TH	K [K]		•							
...NTATION	K [K]		•							

a Argument(s) are not optional for REFERENCE.

...ommand		FIGURE [K K K K]	DATA [K K K K]	LEGEND [K K K K]	NOLEGEND	OVERLAY / NOOVERLAY	SAME [K [K]]	ASPECT K K
	K	•	•	•				
...OR	K	•	•	•				
...E	K	•	•	•				
...OR	K	•	•	•				
...E	K	•	•	•				
		• (default)	• (default)	•				
...IP		•	•	• (default)				
...T	K			•				
...OR	K			•				
...E	K			•				
...E	K			•				
...EMENT	K K			•				
...ET	K K			•				

...mands for Saving and Displaying Graphs ⑨E

...aph command)
...SAVE   ['filename'] (a subcommand of all graph commands)
    REPLACE   (not available for %graphs)
    NOREPLACE   (not available for %graphs)

...   ['filename.mgf'] (if filename is not specified, display 'minitab.mgf')
...E   in multiple graph comand, pause display of each graph until user presses a key [or for K seconds]
...COPY 'format' (**VAX9 Enhanced** only)
...RT ['filename'] (**VAX9 Enhanced** only)
...EPLACE
...OREPLACE

Standard Argument Values ⑨E

Symbol Types

(VAX/VMS has 0 through 5)

0	None	8	⊕	16	◆	24	▷
1	○	9	⊗	17	◇	25	◁
2	+	10	⊙	18	⊕	26	◄
3	×	11	□	19	△	27	◁
4	✳	12	■	20	▲	28	▽
5	· (dot)	13	▢	21	△	29	▼
6	●	14	⊠	22	▷	30	▽
7	○	15	◇	23	►		

Colors

(VAX/VMS has 0 through 7)

0	null (background color)	8	dark red
1	black (foreground color)	9	dark green
2	red	10	dark blue
3	green	11	dark cyan
4	blue	12	dark magenta
5	cyan	13	dark yellow
6	magenta	14	dark gray
7	yellow	15	light gray

Fill Types
(default)

(VAX/VMS has 0 through 7)

0	null (transparent)
1	solid background
2	right hatch foregound
3	left hatch foreground
4	right & left hatch foreground
5	horizontal hatch foreground
6	vertical hatch foreground
7	horizontal & vertical hatch foreground
8	grid foreground
9	squared foreground

Fonts
(default)

Microsoft Windows		**Macintosh**	
0	None	0	None
1	Times New Roman	1	Times
2	Arial	2	Helvetica
3	Courier New	3	Courier
4	Symbol	4	Symbol
5	Wingdings	5	Zapf Dingbats
6...	all installed TrueType fonts		(may differ for before System 7.5)
		6...	all installed fonts (in alphabetical order)

VAX/VMS			
0	None	11	Gothic Italian
1	Simplex Monospace	12	Gothic English
2	Simplex Roman	13	Complex Cyrillic
3	Complex Roman	14	Upper Case Math
4	Duplex Roman	15	Lower Case Math
5	Triplex Roman	16	Music
6	Simplex Script	17	Meteorology
7	Complex Script	18	Symbols
8	Simplex Greek	19	Astrology
9	Complex Greek	20	Complex Italics
10	Gothic German	21	Triplex Italics

(default)

Line Types
(default)

(VAX/VMS has 0 through 4)

0	null (invisible)
1	solid
2	dash
3	dot
4	dash 1-dot
5	dash 2-dots
6	dash 3-dots
7	long dashes

Figure/Page Unit Coordinate Grid ⑨E

aracter (and G-Style Hi-Res) Graphs

cter (or typewriter-style) graphs display in the Session window and do not use any
graphics subcommands described previously. You can save character graphs by
the Session window contents; to save, make the Session window active and
e **File ➤ Save Window As**. High-resolution commands begin with G and exist for
, MPLOT, LPLOT, TPLOT, GBOXPLOT, and GHISTOGRAM.

Session window or Command Line Editor, type the command GSTD (standard
cs) to enable character graphs. To re-enable high-resolution (professional
cs) commands, type GPRO. DOTPLOT and STEM-AND-LEAF character graphs
ailable in GSTD and GPRO mode. When you produce graphs through the menus,
switches modes automatically.

		enable character graphs	
		enable high-resolution graphics	
GRAM	C…C		
LOT	C…C		

GRAM and DOTPLOT have the subcommands:

NCREMENT	= K
TART	at K [end at K]
Y	C
AME	scales for all columns

AND-LEAF	display of C…C
RIM	outliers
NCREMENT	= K
Y	C

LOT	for C
NCREMENT	= K
TART	at K [end at K]
Y	C
NES	= K
OTCH	[K% confidence] sign c.i.
EVELS	K…K

	C vs. C
YMBOL	= 'symbol'
T	C vs. C, and C vs. C, and… C vs. C
	C vs. C using tags in C
	C vs. C vs. C

MPLOT, LPLOT, and TPLOT have the subcommands:

TLE	= 'text'
OOTNOTE	= 'text'
LABEL	= 'text'
LABEL	= 'text'
NCREMENT	= K
START	at K [end at K]
NCREMENT	= K
START	at K [end at K]

, GMPLOT, GLPLOT, and GTPLOT have the subcommands:

| NES | [style K [color K]] connecting points in C C |
| OLOR | C |

TSPLOT	[period K] of C
ORIGIN	= K
MTSPLOT	[period K] of C…C
ORIGIN	= K
ORIGIN	= K for C…C … origin K for C…C

TSPLOT and MTSPLOT have the subcommands:

INCREMENT	= K
START	at K [end at K]
TSTART	at K [end at K]

| GRID | C [K to K] C [K to K] |

CONTOUR	C vs. C and C
BLANK	bands between letters
YSTART	= K [up to K]
YINCREMENT	= K

| WIDTH | of all character plots is K spaces globally |
| HEIGHT | of all character plots is K lines globally |

GOPTIONS	set options for G-style hi-resolution graphics
HEIGHT	= K inches
WIDTH	= K inches
PRINTER	for printer graphics
PLOTTER	for plotter graphics

All G-style high resolution graphics commands have the subcommand

| FILE | 'filename' to store graphics output |

Global and Local Macros (%macros)

Global and local macros use the default file extension MAC and are invoked using the symbol %. You can include a path statement after %.

To execute a global macro, type
    %filename (e.g. *%mymacro* or *%c:\research\mymacro*)

To execute a local macro, type
    %filename arguments;
        subcommandname arguments;

        ...
        subcommandname arguments.

If the macro is in another directory, invoke with a path statement. For example:

Microsoft Windows	*%c:\research\mymacro*
Macintosh	*%mydisk:research:mymacro*
Vax/VMS	*%[research]mymacro*
Unix	*%/usr/local/research/mymacro*

Global Macro Format

Format Elements	Example of ANALYZE.MAC
GMACRO command	GMACRO
template (macro name, usually the same as the macro file name)	Analyze
body of macro	NAME C1 = 'Yield' C2 = 'Chem1' & C5 = 'Ln.Yield' REGRESS C5 2 C1 C2
ENDMACRO command	ENDMACRO
Invoked by typing ...	%ANALYZE

Local Macro Format

Format Elements	Example of GEN2.MAC
MACRO command	MACRO
template (macro name, subcommand names, and argument names in order that they will be invoked)	GEN2 MEDIANS; OBS M.
declaration statements	MCOLUMN X.1-X.M MEDIANS MCONSTANT M
DEFAULT statement (to be used if user does not enter a value for an argument)	DEFAULT M = 5
body of macro	RANDOM 100 X.1-X.M RMEDIAN X.1-X.M MEDIANS
ENDMACRO statement	ENDMACRO
Invoked by typing ...	%GEN2 C1-C5; OBS 10.

Declaration Statements for Local Macros

MCONSTANT	list of variables that are constants
MCOLUMN	list of variables that are columns
MMATRIX	list of variables that are matrices
MFREE	list of variables, type determined when macro executed
DEFAULT	argument = value ... argument=value

Variables in Local Macros

KKCAT	K K K
KKNAME	K C, K C, ...
KKSET	K 'text', K 'text', ...
MTYPE	variable K (local macros only if variable is a constant returns K=1, if a column K=2, if a matrix K=3)

Control Statements for Global and Local Macros

BREAK	goes to the command that follows a DO or WHILE loop
DO	K = list of numbers
ENDDO	
EXIT	stop macro, return to Minitab session
GOTO	number
MLABEL	number (marker for GOTO statement)
IF	logical expression (same as for LET)
ELSEIF	logical expression
ELSE	
ENDIF	
NEXT	transfers control to beginning of DO or WHILE loop
PAUSE	transfers control from macro to keyboard
RESUME	returns control to the macro
WHILE	logical expression
ENDWHILE	

Labeling Output of Global and Local Macros

MTITLE	'title'
TITLE	(default)
NOTITLE	suppress output titles in Session window
WTITLE	'title' for graph window

Debugging Tools for Global and Local Macros

DEBUG	tells how the macro is processing
NODEBUG	(default)
ECHO	displays commands in macro during execution
NOECHO	(default)
SYSTEM	[systemcommand] provides access to DOS
TYPE	'[path]filename.ext' displays a file
PAUSE	
RESUME	

Additional Global and Local Macro Features

CALL	template (calls a subroutine in the same file)
RETURN	
INFO	displays summary of local worksheet
PLUG	macro keeps going when it finds an error
NOPLUG	(default)
MRESET	restore environment settings after macro runs
SWAP	fit macro into available memory
NOSWAP	(default)
BRIEF	= K controls amount of output from ARIMA, BBDESIGN, CCDESIGN, CLUOBS, CLUVARS, DISCRIMINANT, FA, FFDESIGN, GLM, KMEANS, MIXREG, REGRESS, RL, RSREG, SCDESIGN, and SLDESIGN
GPAUSE	[K]
GSCALE	K K
NMINIMUM	K
NMAXIMUM	K
NTICKS	K
TMINIMUM	K
TMAXIMUM	K
TINCREMENT	K
SMINIMUM	K
SMAXIMUM	K

Communicating with Macro Users

FILE	'TERMINAL' subcommand with READ, SET, and INSEF
NOTE	[comment]
YESNO	K (returns K=1 if user responds 'Yes', K=0 for 'No')

Execs

Execs use the default file extension MTB and are invoked using the command EXE

EXECUTE	['filename'] [K times]
NOECHO	do not display the commands that follow
ECHO	display the commands that follow
YESNO	K
STORE	[in 'filename'] the following commands
REPLACE	existing file
NOREPLACE	do not replace existing file
END	of storing commands

Looping Through Columns and Matrices

Use the CK syntax to use a constant to specify a column number. If K1 = 3, then C3; if K2 = 16, then CK2 = C16. Specify a matrix using the MK syntax. Here is an example of an Exec called PLOTS.MTB that uses CK:

                The first time through the loop, K1 = 1, giving
   PLOT C21 * CK1   PLOT C21 * C1. The next time through the loop, K1
   LET K1 = K1 + 1 giving PLOT C21 * C2, and so on.

Start the Exec and generate 20 plots by typing:
LET K1 = 1
EXECUTE 'PLOTS' 20

Appendix B: Data

Finding the Pulse Data

The PULSE.MTW data set appears often throughout this manual and comes with every release of Minitab. Chapters 1 and 2 use it exclusively to illustrate a sample Minitab session. Many of the statistical commands in Chapter 5 and the graphs in Chapter 6 contain examples that use this data set. Different systems require different retrieval instructions, and if your system isn't mentioned below, or if even with these instructions you can't find PULSE.MTW, see your System Administrator for information on the location of the sample Minitab data sets.

System	Path Name
VAX/VMS	'SYS$MINITAB:PULSE'
Sun/SunOS™	'/usr/local/lib/minitab/handbook/pulse'
IBM VM/CMS®	'PULSE'
PRIME®	'MINITAB>HANDBOOK>PULSE'
HP®9000 (Unix)	'/usr/local/minitab/sav/pulse'
Data General®	'PULSE'
Microsoft Windows	'c:\mtbwin\data\pulse'
Macintosh	'pulse'

Description of PULSE.MTW

Students in an introductory statistics course participated in a simple experiment. Each student recorded his or her height, weight, gender, smoking preference, usual activity level, and resting pulse. Then they all flipped coins, and those whose coins came up heads ran in place for one minute. Then the entire class recorded their pulses once more.

Variable	Description
C1 'PULSE1'	Resting pulse rate
C2 'PULSE2'	Second pulse rate
C3 'RAN'	1 = ran in place; 2 = did not run in place
C4 'SMOKES'	1 = smokes regularly; 2 = does not smoke regularly
C5 'SEX'	1 = male; 2 = female
C6 'HEIGHT'	Height in inches
C7 'WEIGHT'	Weight in pounds
C8 'ACTIVITY'	Usual level of physical activity: 1 = slight; 2 = moderate; 3 = a lot

Listing of PULSE.MTW

ROW	PULSE1	PULSE2	RAN	SMOKES	SEX	HEIGHT	WEIGHT	ACTIVITY
1	64	88	1	2	1	66.00	140	2
2	58	70	1	2	1	72.00	145	2
3	62	76	1	1	1	73.50	160	3
4	66	78	1	1	1	73.00	190	1
5	64	80	1	2	1	69.00	155	2
6	74	84	1	2	1	73.00	165	1
7	84	84	1	2	1	72.00	150	3
8	68	72	1	2	1	74.00	190	2
9	62	75	1	2	1	72.00	195	2
10	76	118	1	2	1	71.00	138	2
11	90	94	1	1	1	74.00	160	1
12	80	96	1	2	1	72.00	155	2
13	92	84	1	1	1	70.00	153	3
14	68	76	1	2	1	67.00	145	2
15	60	76	1	2	1	71.00	170	3
16	62	58	1	2	1	72.00	175	3
17	66	82	1	1	1	69.00	175	2
18	70	72	1	1	1	73.00	170	3
19	68	76	1	1	1	74.00	180	2
20	72	80	1	2	1	66.00	135	3
21	70	106	1	2	1	71.00	170	2
22	74	76	1	2	1	70.00	157	2
23	66	102	1	2	1	70.00	130	2
24	70	94	1	1	1	75.00	185	2
25	96	140	1	2	2	61.00	140	2
26	62	100	1	2	2	66.00	120	2
27	78	104	1	1	2	68.00	130	2
28	82	100	1	2	2	68.00	138	2
29	100	115	1	1	2	63.00	121	2
30	68	112	1	2	2	70.00	125	2
31	96	116	1	2	2	68.00	116	2
32	78	118	1	2	2	69.00	145	2
33	88	110	1	1	2	69.00	150	2
34	62	98	1	1	2	62.75	112	2
35	80	128	1	2	2	68.00	125	2
36	62	62	2	2	1	74.00	190	1
37	60	62	2	2	1	71.00	155	2
38	72	74	2	1	1	69.00	170	2
39	62	66	2	2	1	70.00	155	2
40	76	76	2	2	1	72.00	215	2
41	68	66	2	1	1	67.00	150	2
42	54	56	2	1	1	69.00	145	2
43	74	70	2	2	1	73.00	155	3
44	74	74	2	2	1	73.00	155	2
45	68	68	2	2	1	71.00	150	3
46	72	74	2	1	1	68.00	155	3
47	68	64	2	2	1	69.50	150	3
48	82	84	2	1	1	73.00	180	2
49	64	62	2	2	1	75.00	160	3
50	58	58	2	2	1	66.00	135	3

ROW	PULSE1	PULSE2	RAN	SMOKES	SEX	HEIGHT	WEIGHT	ACTIVITY
51	54	50	2	2	1	69.00	160	2
52	70	62	2	1	1	66.00	130	2
53	62	68	2	1	1	73.00	155	2
54	48	54	2	1	1	68.00	150	0
55	76	76	2	2	1	74.00	148	3
56	88	84	2	2	1	73.50	155	2
57	70	70	2	2	1	70.00	150	2
58	90	88	2	1	1	67.00	140	2
59	78	76	2	2	1	72.00	180	3
60	70	66	2	1	1	75.00	190	2
61	90	90	2	2	1	68.00	145	1
62	92	94	2	1	1	69.00	150	2
63	60	70	2	1	1	71.50	164	2
64	72	70	2	2	1	71.00	140	2
65	68	68	2	2	1	72.00	142	3
66	84	84	2	2	1	69.00	136	2
67	74	76	2	2	1	67.00	123	2
68	68	66	2	2	1	68.00	155	2
69	84	84	2	2	2	66.00	130	2
70	61	70	2	2	2	65.50	120	2
71	64	60	2	2	2	66.00	130	3
72	94	92	2	1	2	62.00	131	2
73	60	66	2	2	2	62.00	120	2
74	72	70	2	2	2	63.00	118	2
75	58	56	2	2	2	67.00	125	2
76	88	74	2	1	2	65.00	135	2
77	66	72	2	2	2	66.00	125	2
78	84	80	2	2	2	65.00	118	1
79	62	66	2	2	2	65.00	122	3
80	66	76	2	2	2	65.00	115	2
81	80	74	2	2	2	64.00	102	2
82	78	78	2	2	2	67.00	115	2
83	68	68	2	2	2	69.00	150	2
84	72	68	2	2	2	68.00	110	2
85	82	80	2	2	2	63.00	116	1
86	76	76	2	1	2	62.00	108	3
87	87	84	2	2	2	63.00	95	3
88	90	92	2	1	2	64.00	125	1
89	78	80	2	2	2	68.00	133	1
90	68	68	2	2	2	62.00	110	2
91	86	84	2	2	2	67.00	150	3
92	76	76	2	2	2	61.75	108	2

INDEX

CAPITAL LETTERS denote commands and subcommands. Subcommands are listed followed by the main command in parentheses. **Bold Letters** denote a menu path. Final menu/dialog box choices are listed followed by the first part of the path in parentheses.

N

NAME 2-12, 4-9

name columns

Data window 4-5

session commands 4-9

navigate the Data window 4-7

new features in this release xii

Next Row/Column (Editor) 4-7

NOJOURNAL 3-7

NOOUTFILE 2-15, 4-16, A-3

%NORMPLOT A-19

numeric data 3-12

O

OH 2-5, 3-13

OMIT subcommand with COPY 5-3

one-sample t-test 5-17

ONEWAY analysis of variance 2-10, 5-22

Oneway (Stat ➤ ANOVA) 1-12, 5-22

online Help, see Help

Open Graph (File) 4-19

Open Worksheet (File) 1-4, 4-17, 4-19

operations 5-9

precedence 5-13

option button 3-5

optional argument 3-10

OUTFILE 2-3, 4-16, 4-18, A-3

outfile

save character-based graph (see graph, save) 6-9

save session 4-16

P

paired data

confidence interval 5-16

t-test 5-18

pairwise deletion 5-20

Paste (Edit) 5-2

paste in the Data window 4-8

Paste/Insert Cells (Edit) 4-6, 4-8

Paste/Replace Cells (Edit) 4-8

patterned data 4-13

PC 1-2, 3-2

Pearson product moment 5-19

percentages of columns 5-24

pi, as stored constant 3-8

PLOT 2-14, 6-3

Plot (Graph) 1-18, 6-3

point using a mouse 3-4

PORTABLE subcommand, with RETRIEVE 4-18

portable worksheet 4-19

precedence of operations 5-13

PREDICT subcommand, with REGRESS 5-21

prediction intervals 5-21

preferences

Graph windows A-5

PRINT 2-5, 4-10, 4-18

print 4-18

graph 6-9

window, including worksheet, graphs, session, and so on 4-18

worksheet using session commands 4-18

Print Window (File) 4-18, 6-9

process control chart 6-7

product information xi

prompt 3-13

CONT> 3-13

Continue? 2-5, 3-13

DATA> 2-8, 3-13, 4-10

MTB> 2-3, 2-6, 3-3, 3-6, 3-8, 3-13

SUBC> 2-6, 3-9, 3-13

PULSE.MTW

description 1-2, B-1

listing B-2

punctuation for command language 3-9

Q

quartile 5-14

Quick Reference Card x

Quit (File) 1-20, 3-3

quotation marks around column names 4-9

R

RANK 5-20

Rank (Manip) 5-2, 5-20

READ 4-9, 4-10, 4-18

FORMAT 4-10, 4-18

recalling the last dialog box A-2

recording a session A-3

Reference Manual x

registered Minitab users xi

REGRESS 5-20

regression 1-19, 2-14

Regression (Stat ➤ Regression) 5-20

releases of Minitab 1-2, 3-2

repetitive data entry 4-13

U

undo a change in the Data window 4-4

Undo Change Within Cell (Edit) 4-6

Undo Cut/Paste (Edit) 4-8

Undo (Edit) 4-4

UNIX 3-2

Unstack (Manip) 5-2

upper control limit 6-7

uppercase 3-10, 4-9

USE subcommand, with
  COPY 2-12, 5-3

V

variables 3-5, 3-8

VAX/VMS 3-2

W

width of columns, change 4-6

windows in Minitab 3-5

work with menus 3-4

worksheet 3-8
 convert to text file 4-16
 current 4-14
 edit 1-7, 2-6, 2-7, 4-2
 edit with LET 4-11
 information 3-6
 manipulate using session
  commands 4-9
 manipulate with cut, copy, and
  paste 4-8
 open 1-4

portable 4-19

print 4-18

restore 4-6

retrieve 4-17

save 4-14

save in other formats 4-15

select for cut and paste 4-8

summary 2-4, 3-6

view data 1-5, 2-5, 4-10

WRITE 4-16, 4-18

X

Xbar (Stat ➤ Control Charts) 6-7

XBARCHART 6-7

How to Order Additional Products

Additional Documentation

Minitab Inc. offers clearly-written documentation to assist Minitab users in installing, running, and applying Minitab functionality to statistical problem solving.

MINITAB Reference Manual

- Release 10*Xtra* for Windows
- Release 10*Xtra* for Macintosh

A complete and detailed manual covering all commands, with numerous examples throughout.

MINITAB User's Guide

- Release 10*Xtra* for Windows
- Release 10*Xtra* for Macintosh

A complete guide to getting started with Minitab for Windows or Macintosh, Release 10*Xtra*, including installation, sample sessions, and lots of Windows- or Macintosh-specific information to get you "up and running" quickly.

MINITAB Reference Manual

- Release 9 for Windows
- Release 8, PC Version
- Release 7
- Release 9 (for OpenVMS, Unix)
- Release 8, Macintosh Version

A complete and detailed manual covering all commands, step-by-step instructions, sample sessions, and system-specific information. The *MINITAB Reference Manual* for Release 9 documents the features available in the Standard Version of Minitab and Minitab for Windows.

MINITAB Graphics Manual

- Release 9 for Windows
- Release 9 (for OpenVMS, Unix)

A comprehensive guide, filled with examples and detailed information on how to use Professional Graphics commands, available with the Enhanced Version of Minitab and Minitab for Windows.

MINITAB QC Manual

- Release 9 for Windows
- Release 9 (for OpenVMS, Unix)

A comprehensive guide on how to use Minitab's quality control and improvement features, including statistical process control charts and design of experiments capabilities, available with the Enhanced Version of Minitab and Minitab for Windows.

MINITAB QC Supplement, Release 8

A supplement to the Release 8 *MINTAB Reference Manual* that documents additional quality control and improvement capabilities included in Release 8 of Minitab. (Automatically included with purchase of Release 8 *MINITAB Reference Manual*; not available independently.)

MINITAB Quick Reference Card

- Release 10*Xtra* for Windows
- Release 10*Xtra* for Macintosh
- Release 9 for Windows
- Release 9
- Release 8, PC Version
- Release 8, Macintosh Version
- Release 7

A convenient, small card or booklet that summarizes all Minitab commands.

MINITAB Handbook, Third Edition[*]

A supplementary text that teaches basic statistics using Minitab. The Handbook features the creative use of plots, application of standard statistical methods to real data, in-depth exploration of data, and more.

[*] If ordering only this text, contact Wadsworth Publishing: In the USA, call 800-354-9706. Outside the USA, call: 606-282-5786.

MINITAB Mini-Manual

An inexpensive beginner's guide that explains the fundamentals of using Minitab—how to enter commands, how to manage and manipulate data and files, and more. You can use it with any current version of Minitab, including Release 10.

To order, contact your distributor or call Minitab Inc. between 8:30 a.m. and 5:30 p.m. Eastern time, Monday through Friday. If you are calling from within the U.S. or Canada, call 800-448-3555. Otherwise, call 814-238-3280, or contact Minitab Inc. at the address listed on the back of this manual or via e-mail at sales@minitab.com.

Minitab is Available for Over 30 Platforms

Minitab Statistical Software is available for PC and Macintosh microcomputer systems. Minitab is also available for mainframes, minicomputers, and workstations including Data General, DEC, Hewlett-Packard, IBM, Prime, Sun, and others.

For additional information contact:

Minitab Inc.
800-448-3555 from within U.S. or Canada
814-238-3280 from outside U.S. or Canada
3081 Enterprise Drive
State College, PA 16801–3008 USA
email: sales@minitab.com

or your distributor. The next page, entitled "Minitab Distributors," lists distributor contact information.

SCAN Software for Chemometric Analysis

SCAN is comprehensive yet easy to use software for chemometric analysis. Its wide range of state-of-the-art methods includes exploratory data analysis, classification, regression (calibration), modern validation and diagnostic techniques, data preprocessing, and a large collection of graphics displays. SCAN is available for Windows machines.

Minitab Distributors

Minitab Inc.
3081 Enterprise Drive
State College, PA 16801-3008
USA
Tel: 1-814-238-3280
Fax: 1-814-238-4383
Customer Support: 1-814-231-2682
e-mail: sales@minitab.com
(Worldwide—countries not
listed elsewhere on this page.)

Asia-Pacific

SIR Pty Ltd
10-18 Cliff Street
Milsons Point NSW 2061
Australia
Tel: 61 2 99 29 74 66
Fax: 61 2 99 29 74 98
e-mail: minitab@sir.com.au
(Australia, New Zealand)

Tek-Hand Corporation
8F-3, #30,
Chung Shan N Rd., Sec. 3
Taipei
Taiwan (R.O.C.)
Tel: 886-2-585-1367
Fax: 886-2-585-0919
(Taiwan, Korea, Japan,
Thailand, Indonesia)

Europe

Minitab Ltd.
3 Mercia Business Village
Torwood Close
Westwood Business Park
Coventry, England
CV4 8HX
Tel: 44-1203-695730
Fax: 44-1203-695731
Toll-free in the UK: 0500-586587
Toll-free in Norway: 8-00-11056
Toll-free in France: 0590-84-54
(UK, Ireland, Belgium, Denmark,
Finland, France, Norway, Sweden,
Switzerland)

IQBAL EDV-Systeme
Heiser Weg 51
27616 Hollen
Germany
Tel: 49-4748-94990
Fax: 49-4748-949931
(Austria, Germany, Switzerland)

CompuDrug Chemistry
Holán Erno u. 5
H-1136 Budapest
Hungary
Tel: 36-1-1326-381
Fax: 36-1-1322-574
(Hungary, Slovakia, Czech
Republic, Slovenia, Poland,
Ukraine, Russia)

TR, Technical Research
Mallorca, 250 ático
08008 Barcelona
Spain
Tel: 34-3-691-8972
      34-3-580-7307
Fax: 34-3-580-1006
      34-3-216-0681
(Spain, Portugal, Italy)

Latin America

Compumática, Inc.
Paseo de la Reforma 324, Suite 110
Colonia Juárez
06605 México, D.F.
Mexico
Tel: 52-5-533-5389
Fax: 52-5-533-5389
(Mexico, Latin America)

Compumática, Inc.
484 Washington St., B-206
Monterey, CA 93940
Tel: 408-648-3506
Fax: 408-646-0951
e-mail: PFields@compumatica.com
(Mexico, Latin America)

AIDE Consultores SRL
Bartolomé Mitre 1617,
Ofc 301
1037 Buenes Aires
Argentina
Tel: 54-1-371-6582
Fax: 54-1-371-6582 (same)
(Argentina, Uruguay)